D1093984

Verena Gurtner
The Schilthorn Roundabout

Foreword

When writing a travel book, the first question to be considered is whether the reader will be using it on the journey, before setting out or as a means of refreshing his memory afterwards.

This little book is intended to serve in all three cases. In spite of all that has been packed into it, it is neither bulky nor heavy, the text is calculated to heighten the pleasure with which the reader looks forward to an exciting experience, and carefully selected photographs, together with explanations, help him to a better understanding of what he has seen when reviewing the tour afterwards. The author has tried to avoid being monotonous and superficial, aiming rather at being lighthearted, understandable and accurate to ensure that the book will afford many trippers and "organized tourists" chasing from peak to peak a few hours of pleasure experiencing the Schilthorn in retrospect.

The reader must excuse the fact that a fair portion of technology and a brief history of cable railways in general have gatecrashed on this invitation to visit the Schilthorn, the hinterland of Mürren, Gimmelwald and Lauterbrunnen and these magical villages themselves, all so rich in tradition (or was it perhaps the mountains and villages that gatecrashed on the technohistorical part!?). Looking beyond the subject of immediate interest helps to introduce variety and a rainbow thread into the flow of the story. Thus, the reader interested in things technical will find here – independent of mountain and countryside and following on from the Strub, Riggenbach, Abt and Locher rack-and-pinion systems described in earlier works – the completion of the mountain railway theme with the story of the creation and functioning of cable railways, above all of aerial cableways, together with the necessary tables and explanations.

James Bond has, of course, not been forgotten. There is a résumé on p. 16 of the story of 007's adventures on "Piz Gloria" (alias the Schilthorn) for anyone who has not read the book or seen the film – or has forgotten what it was all about.

Choose a fine day and enjoy yourself treading in 007's footsteps!

V.G.

Verena Gurtner

The Schilthorn Roundabout

Portrait of an Aerial Cableway

26 full-colour plates
80 black-and-white illustrations
Panoramas and Maps
8 Tables

Translated by Kay Gillioz-Pettigrew

Orell Füssli Publishers Zurich

1st English edition 1978
Original title "Schilthorn umsteigen – Konterfei der Luftseilbahn",
Orell Füssli Zürich, 1978

Also by Verena Gurtner:
"Jungfrau Express"
"Gornergrat Return"
"Mount Pilatus via Lucerne"

Produced by Dr. Verena Gurtner
Set, printed and bound by Brügger, Meiringen
Reproductions by Aberegg-Steiner, Berne
Printed in Switzerland
ISBN 3 280 01010 1

Contents

The Challenge

Hidden amidst the innocent green of forest and pastureland is a determined little siren whose only aim in life is to batten on to any unsuspecting four-legged creature that happens to be passing. Quick as lightning, it drops into the warm fur and hangs on like grim death, sapping the poor creature's life-blood, until it is satiated. And the wretched thing is so prolific, the chances of ever getting the better of it are negligible.

This little pest has certain characteristics in common with the mountains. There is this tendency, particularly on the part of the towering walls in Lauterbrunnen Valley, to pounce on the unsuspecting visitor. These mountains are so sombre, shadowy and shapelessly vast, so massively towering and dripping wet that they tend at first to stifle good humour, with their long-fingered shadows creeping down one's neck and up one's sleeves.

But a second look will show that this is nonsense! There are those stiff little clouds rippling across the blue vault of heaven – even if heaven seems rather a long way away – and a gilded white diadem is shining on the horizon. Soft winds and cloud, rain and sun chase each other endlessly through the valley – that is the *foehn,* the south wind. The atmosphere changes in the twinkling of an eye, each change reflected in the bright windows of the houses tucked into the folds of the earth.

And each time the veil lifts, the storm-swept fir-trees seem to have climbed higher up the rock face and the mountaintops appear even further away than they did the day before – as if they had grown a couple of ca-

Life's more modest pleasures can be wrung from even the hardest winter and the dwindling tilth by the application of intelligence, determined effort and a fathom or two of dry wood under the eaves. Here, houses, tillage and pasture turn sunwards and a taciturn humour helps keep the shadows at bay.

▶ *Even when the 3437 metres of the neighbouring Gspaltenhorn harbours the menace of avalanche, it's business as usual in the valley below! View from Birg Station on the Schilthorn Cableway.*

Up, up and away! Free balloons float off from Lauterbrunnen Valley towards Italy, leaving the ice-wall of the Gletscherhorn far below. In 1910 Captain Edouard Spelterini undertook the first crossing of the Alps in his air-balloon, "Sirius", taking off from Mürren and landing in Lanzo Torinese behind the Gran Paradiso.

thedral-tower lengths in the lee of the drizzle during the night. For yesterday we could look the mountain straight in the eye, man to man, and today we have to bend over backwards and crick our necks just to see its broad breast. Memory is as deceptive as any photograph: it has the same foreshortening effect as the perspective and the might of the mountains will always be elusive and defy description – most of all in the Valley of Lauterbrunnen.

◄◄ *8 o'clock on a May morning up on the Schilthorn terrace. The lure of the mountains makes itself felt as far away as New York and Paris, Bonn and Copenhagen. Up on the Schilthorn, the city dweller is just near enough to the Alps to be able to enjoy their beauty at a distance easy on the eye, and yet to feel comfortably safeguarded against their dangers. These early birds have two "petrified" ladies, part of the Blümlisalp group (right), in their sights – the Weisse Frau between the Morgenhorn and the Blümlisalphorn and the Wilde Frau above the Sefinenfurgge saddle, the pass between the Lauterbrunnen and Kander Valleys. Left, the Gspaltenhorn, the Hintere and Vordere Büttlassen. The last of the spring storms has blown red Sahara dust over névé and snow.*

10

In 1957 Captain Fred Dolder repeated Spelterini's flight in his balloon, "Zurich". Today, free-balloon flyers from all over the world flock to Mürren every year where the International High-Alpine Dolder Ballooning Weeks are still held. On the right is the Aletschhorn (4195 m) with its long north-east ridge so popular among alpine skiers.

But try convincing God's two-legged creatures of this fact. There's that merry-eyed little person, pointing with one hand to the wild Breithorn Glacier at the edge of the sky and holding a cup in the other as she enquires how far she has to go. On being given an answer, she climbs on with verve along the stony upward path, for she has promised her children a handful of that gleaming whiteness. There's nothing like burning your boats for getting you somewhere!

People instinctively divide up into digestible portions anything that is too big and then tackle it bit by bit. Thus, the mountain is mustered from summit to foot and back again. The eye automatically catalogues the successive phases of the ascent – a scree here, a patch of forest there, angled slabs of red rock, paler ribbons of limestone, gulleys, a looped and scaly sheet of rock, velvety dark slate, a frieze of fir-trees, a niche in a green ledge. The mountain is perfectly negotiable – how could it be otherwise? One last culvert and the difficulties would seem to be overcome. The mustering

'Carefree skiers racing over the wintry slopes of the Schilthorn. The peak is the starting point of the legendary Inferno Race which is to the downhill enthusiast what the Engadine marathon is to the cross-country skier. The piste – never specially beaten – drops 2000 m over the 12 kilometres of its length between the peak and Lauterbrunnen. Before the cableway was built the skiers had to do the trip to the top of the Schilthorn on foot.

glance travels upwards, seeking and testing each foothold on the ascending path.

The point of no return has already been left behind and the mountain has a firm hold on its victim, fanning the spark of dreams and whipping ambitious desires into wakefulness. To fathom the unknown and risk one's all, to grapple, dissect, catalogue and paragraph until all the earth's secrets lie revealed – man's thirst for knowledge and clarity, for the glory of the heights and the wide-open spaces, for room to move, the right to do as he pleases and for sunlight and the deep wells of quietude, is as old as time itself. And man progresses, both as an individual and as a species.

It is less the whims of Nature than man's own resources – his physical strength, his willpower, imagination and energy – which decide the question of progress and setback. In Lauterbrunnental he is going to need every last ounce of those resources plus a goodly store of patience. Nowhere else in the Alps do the mountains conspire so successfully to form such a forbidding

Construction of the cableway was nearing completion when the producer of the James Bond films started looking for just such an installation for the filming of Ian Fleming's "On Her Majesty's Secret Service." Thus it was that Commander Bond, Count Balthasar de Bleuville and his ten beauties were among the very first passengers on the brand-new Schilthorn gondolas. "On Her Majesty's Secret Service" was filmed in 1968/69.

Main specifications of the Schilthorn Cableway

Mode of operation	Dual-cable aerial cableway of the to-and-fro system
Number of sections	4
Number of stations	5 and one intermediate stopping-place
Length of line	6931 m
Total ascent	2103 m from the lower to the upper terminus
Intermediate supports	6
Number of cabins	5
Travelling time	21 min
Driving system	Ward-Leonard

wall, towering steeply to thousands of feet. From Grindelwald to Peters-grat, from the Eiger to the Breithorn stretches a 20-kilometre-long line, pegged to which is a neatly smoothed pinafore, rock-gored, glacier-pocketed and hung about with lacy frills and looped ribbons. In the background lies a labyrinthine world of telescoped bulges of ice and intertwined glaciers – the

entrails of the mountain where an attack of hiccoughs raises the water-level in Europe's rivers – the Rhone, the Rhine and the Po; for this washing-line is nothing other than the gigantic front wall of the Aare and the Gotthard Massifs and the watershed of the Continent – pioneer country. (See white part of the map on p. 29.)

Here come the first pioneers already, with the lichens drumming them in. With the help of dust, sunshine, air and water, they weave that gaily coloured carpet and spread it over the rock. The dainty ranunculus glacialis brings on the alpine flora, its pink and white flowers on a velvety calyx always cocking a snook at the scree on the windswept peak. Then come the rank and file – the androsaces and saxifrages which upholster those little green cushions in the rocky wilderness. The mountain alder holds the glacial drift together and slowly but surely patches of grass and forest start appearing.

From the tree-line downwards the process is reversed and the mountain firs are felled to open up pastureland for the cattle. Progressive man comes with spade, mattock and crowbar, with pickaxe and scythe, ladder and alpenstock, with barometer, hygrometer, drawing-block and plumbline – to plan and to build.

◀ *Spelterini used to take camera and photographic plates on his balloon flights. In 1910 he took the picture on the left showing the Jungfrau with the hanging Giessen glacier. The dotted line indicates the north-wall route opened up fourteen years later by Hans Lauper and Pierre von Schumacher. In the nineteen-twenties, when all the alpine peaks had been "done", mountaineers turned their attention to the steep north-walls edging the Alps.*

Science aims high as well – the Sphinx Observatory at 3573 m. It was Adolf Guyer-Zeller's promise to help set up a scientific research station which persuaded Parliament to grant the concession for his Jungfrau Railway in 1894. The effects of great heights upon the human organism were not yet fully understood; Spelterini, the balloonist, supported Guyer by confirming that heights were harmless and that the body adapted itself.

Slow Waltz by Snowlight

The only pioneer who just arrived and helped himself to the mountains without previously engaging in any of the customary back-breaking effort (beyond paying the expenses) was James Bond; he simply made use of the brand-new Schilthorn cableway for as long as it suited his convenience.

In March and June 1965 the lower sections of the Schilthorn cableway went into operation and subsequently served as a display piece for the uppermost section which was opened on 12th June 1967. The cable railway rises in four sections from the trough of Stechelberg, via six masts and a string of superlatives, towards the sunwashed peak where it proffers its invitation to the waltz, to the accompaniment of the revolving restaurant crowning the peak.

As the longest of Europe's cableways, stretching over a full seven thousand metres and leaping two thousand at one fell swoop between the fifth mast and Birg, with wind velocities of up to 180 km/h and counterweight shafts penetrating to depths of between 25 and 21 metres, all topped with that elegant carrousel of a restaurant whose windows afford a constantly changing view of the major alpine bulwarks – thirteen famous north walls and forty-three glaciers –, the Schilthorn was God's gift to a superman like James Bond. It was a foregone conclusion that he would choose this spectacular location for the filming of his most dangerous mission. The rotating restaurant at the peak of the Schilthorn was just one year old and still had no name. It was baptized "Piz Gloria" and in the film the name also applied to the mountain.

Between Stechelberg and Spiggengrund, Piz Gloria looks a bit like an orchid in an onion-bed. Everyone knew that it was supposed to be in the Engadine, not far from Piz Bernina, for it was thence that Ian Fleming despatched James Bond on a chase after an unscrupulous criminal that took 007 across England, France and Switzerland and through the twenty-six chapters of his red-hot bestseller, "On Her Majesty's Secret Service." Our hero met Tracy, the girl with the shocking-pink headscarf, at the Casino in Royale-les-Eaux. She played for high stakes and went roaring through the

James Bond amidst the Schilthorn cables? No, this man is overhauling the intermediate suspension below Birg Station. Don't worry – he has to wear a special safety harness to keep him from falling! Between the last mast above Mürren and Birg the 40 mm thick cable hangs free over a distance of nearly 2 km. The two 30 mm thick traction cables glide over cable sheaves in the middle of the suspension between the two carrier cables with a 55 cm gauge. On the right are the cables for the "on-coming" traffic with the emergency cables in the middle.

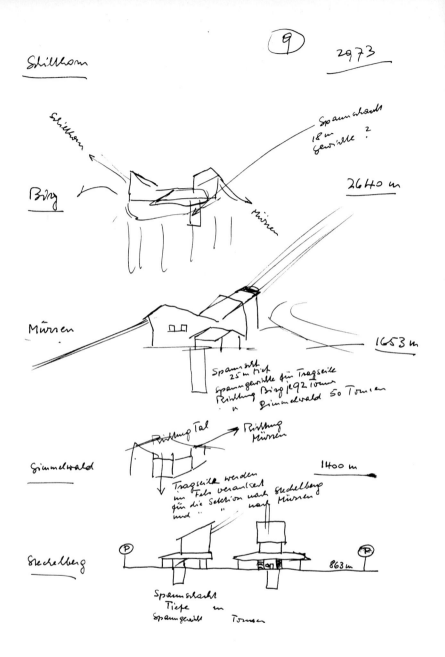

An extract from the file of the initiator of the Schilthorn Cableway, Ernst Feuz, who grew up in Mürren. The cableway was to lead in four sections directly from the Stechelberg carpark to the Schilthorn peak two thousand metres above. The Schilthorn Committee applied for a federal licence on 3rd October 1959.

The sunwashed village of Mürren buried in the snow. The inhabitants are grateful to rest their eyes on the dark cape of the Schwarzmönch after the dazzle of the eternal snow on the surrounding peaks. The deep trough of Lauterbrunnen Valley – not visible here – stretches between the triumvirate of the Eiger, Mönch and Jungfrau and the village.

surrounding countryside in her sleekly expensive car at speeds rivalling those of the wind up on the Schilthorn. It was Tracy who appeared at the fancy-dress ball in Samaden on Christmas Eve, just in time to spirit an injured and exhausted James Bond away from his pursuers. According to 007, "three and a half got themselves killed one way and another" in the heat of the fray: the first at the peak, the second was overtaken by an avalanche loosed on the Gspaltenhorn, the "half" was harpooned by 007's ski-stick and the third was caught in the murderous blades of a snowfan. Apart from that, everything went off satisfactorily – except, perhaps, for the poor man who was catapulted head first down the blue gulch of the bob-run without benefit of sleigh.

But to come to the point – the Schilthorn alias Piz Gloria was the stronghold of an unscrupulous pseudo-scientist bent on ruining the British Isles, to which ends he had installed laboratories for research into biological warfare. Ten unsuspecting British beauties, suitably brainwashed under hypnosis in the seclusion of the remote mountain fastness, were to propagate a killer virus among the cattle of England's green and pleasant land. The enterprise was cleverly camouflaged by the tourist traffic on the cableway. But our pseudo-scientist had a fatal weakness – he was vain. Ernst Stavro Blofeld called himself Count Balthasar de Bleuville and sought with the aid of the College of Arms in London to authenticate his claim to be of aristocratic descent. This gave James Bond, Agent No. 007 on Her Britannic Majesty's secret service, precisely the excuse he required to pose as an expert in heraldry and so to obtain a toehold in the mountain eyrie of Piz Gloria whose entrance hall was adorned with the "family" escutcheon. That entrance hall looks exactly the same today, except that the carpet has in the meantime disintegrated under the shoes of three million Schilthorn visitors. But behind the great open fireplace in the roundabout restaurant the youthful silhouette of 007 and the profiles of ten pretty faces still hang.

With due deference to our hero, the visitor is free to glance through the windows from time to time and to enjoy the pure enchantment of the view spread out under a magic interplay of light and colour while the Piz Gloria

The soil is scanty and the tilth is husbanded by terracing. The welcome francs spent by the beauty-seeking tourists help to swell the meagre fortunes of the less fortunate mountain dwellers.

tables gently follow their 380° path, driven by a little 1.5 horsepower motor. The Schilthorn has the unique advantage of being situated on an isolated turret in front of the main chain of the Alps (see pp. 24/25). There is neither peak nor ridge of similar or greater height in the immediate vicinity of the massif to spoil the view across the wide horizon.

To understand the peak formation, we shall have to turn our attention to a different kind of story and drag our gaze away from the high Alps to concentrate on the dawn of history. It may sound paradoxical, but deep-sea diving is a necessary discipline in any dealings with mountains, for the origins of these vast rock formations must never be forgotten. They derive from the remains of animal and plant organisms which settled in their myriads in the primeval slime of the former Mediterranean, the Thetys, throughout millions of years. Conches and snail-shells built up a vast residue several thousand metres thick, each layer of which was characterized by the deposits that happened to predominate in a particular area. This floor stretched under the growing weight of rock and at intervals a great

It is early spring and a golden day is heralded over Breithorn and Tschingelhorn, promising sunny hours for the Schilthorn tour. An early start will almost certainly be rewarded by a clear view.

spout of molten magma shot into the earth's crust and solidified to form a granite block. Under the increased pressure of Palaeozoic orogenesis or mountain-folding towards the end of the Palaeozoic era, these sediments and intrusive rocks underwent a complete transformation. The result was the materials from which the Bernese Alps are fashioned – crystalline slate and, above all, gneisses.

The finds in the rocks tell that the ocean floor was repeatedly dammed up, dried out and reflooded. The detritus of the old mountain trunk and the material eliminated from the neighbouring mainland intermingled to form yet more new layers. While palm trees waved on the shores of the equatorial Mediterranean and dinosaurs with horny tails and bony collars still existed, the building materials for the Aare Massif were still simmering in the northern shelf of the Mediterranean Sea. In the turbulent phase of the northerly drift and the Alpine upheaval the layers were wedged rather as if pillows had been pushed under blankets and mattresses laid over bedsteads. The Alps were drawn during more recent phases of the Earth's history into this adventurous journey which transformed countryside, climate, flora and fauna – namely during the closing Cretaceous and the dawning Tertiary period; and they had barely arrived when they were promptly overwhelmed by the Ice Age.

Raymond Loewy of New York designed a revolving, double-decker panorama gondola for the Schilthorn Cableway. As this new-fangled device was rejected by the supervisory authorities out of consideration for passengers subject to vertigo, Ernst Feuz decided that the restaurant at the peak should rotate.

◄◄ The experts landed by helicopter on the yet virgin Schilthorn inspecting the site of the upper terminus. Ebnefluh, Mittaghorn and Grosshorn watch the proceedings with interest.

This massive, long-distance transport began 100 million years ago. At that time the pressure of the old African continent in its northerly drift – believed to be connected with the rotation of the earth – caught up the former Mediterranean. The ocean floor was raised, starting with the southern part, and then folded and tipped over in layers towards the north. While most of the folds "floated" uprooted over an unrelated foundation, the Aare Massif was pressed upwards from vast depths, like the Mont Blanc Massif and the Aiguilles Rouges further west, without being uprooted. Its most northerly folds were forced against the old European continent and then dramatically steepled, line ahead, in the seam before Lauterbrunnen – anchored to the rigid rootstock and standing stiffly to attention. The younger Helvetic strata of the same northerly Mediterranean region stretched from Gspaltenhorn to Hohgant. But over these, like the leaves of an artichoke, were drawn "pennine" layers scraped from the ocean depths and

▶▶ The revolving restaurant, "Piz Gloria" – as it was called in the James Bond film –, on the Schilthorn peak. The upper floor, complete with tables and chairs, turns full circle in an hour, parading before the eyes of the diners all the famous silhouettes in the magnificent panorama. The photographs on pp. 40/41, 8/9, 72/73, 84, 85 and 56/57 show the various sections of this panorama (in clockwise order).

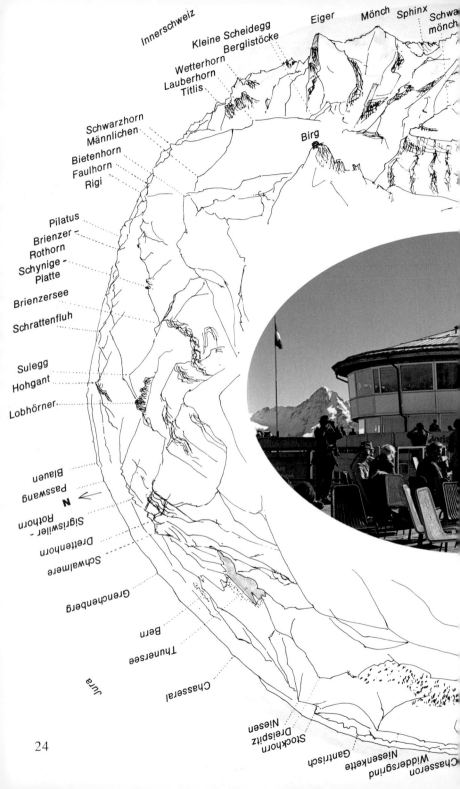

Innerschweiz
Kleine Scheidegg
Berglistöcke
Eiger   Mönch   Sphinx   Schwa
mönch
Wetterhorn
Lauberhorn
Titlis

Schwarzhorn
Männlichen
Birg

Bietenhorn
Faulhorn
Rigi

Pilatus
Brienzer –
Rothorn
Schynige –
Platte
Brienzersee
Schrattenfluh

Sulegg
Hohgant
Lobhörner

Blauen
Passwang
N
Sigriswiler –
Rothorn
Drettenhorn
Schwalmere
Grenchenberg
Bern
Thunersee
Jura
Chasseral
Stockhorn
Dreispitz
Niesen
Gantrisch
Niesenkette
Widdersgrind
Chasseron

Gletscherhorn
Rottal Ebnefluh
gfrau
Mittaghorn
Grosshorn
Schmadrijoch
Lötschental
Breithorn
Tschingelgrat
Tschingelhorn
Tschingelspitz
→ S
Gspaltenhorn
Petersgrat
Büttlassen
Morgen-
horn
Weisse Frau
Blümlisalphorn
Wilde Frau
Doldenhorn
Hundsfluh
Aiguille Verte
Montblanc
Hundshorn
Wildstrubel
Wildhorn
Lohner
Wild Andrist
Albristhorn
Aermighorn
Zahm Andrist
Spilgerten Hohniesen
Savoyen
Bachflüh

25

scales of east alpine strata shipped from the southern belt of shallows. It was left to the wind, the glaciers and the water to blow and lick off the outer scales again and to lay bear the heart. In the Lauterbrunnental this was done so thoroughly that the amazed geologists are still busy collecting. The region has been the subject of intensive study for a hundred and fifty years.

That is the story of the awesome old crystalline rock comprising the queenly Jungfrau and her satellites to right and left. It is also the story of the

Technical data on the four sections of the Schilthorn Cableway

Main Specifications	1st Section Stechelberg– Gimmelwald	2nd Section Gimmelwald– Mürren	3rd Section Mürren– Birg	4th Section Birg– Schilthorn
Date of opening	23. 6. 1965	23. 6. 1965	13. 3. 1965	12. 6. 1967
Lower terminus platform (metres above sea-level)	875	1375	1646	2684
Upper terminus platform (metres above sea-level)	1376	1645	2685	2967
Total ascent	501 m	270 m	1039 m	283 m
Length of line	1188 m	1198 m	2779 m	1766 m
Maximum gradient	1 : 2	1 : 4	1 : 2.4	1 : 3.8
Carrier cables each track	2	2	2	2
Counterweight shaft in	Stechelberg	Mürren	Mürren	Birg
Intermediate supports	1	2	2	1
Maximum free span	1108 m	549 m	1941 m	1738 m
Number of cabins	1	1	2	1
Passengers per cabin	100	100	80	100
Gross weight per cabin	12 200 kg	12 000 kg	10 500 kg	12 300 kg
Upper traction cables	2	2	2	1
Lower traction cables	1	1	2	1
Speed of cabin	8 m/s	8 m/s	10 m/s	10 m/s
Travelling time	4½ min	4½ min	7½ min	4½ min
Driving gear in	Mürren	Mürren	Mürren	Birg
Average motor capacity	460 kW	460 kW	420 kW	330 kW
Maximum motor capacity	750 kW	750 kW	720 kW	500 kW
Hourly passenger capacity in one direction	520	520	550	550

more recent Dogger Bank, part of the foundations of the Helvetic shelf which rolled over the heads of its betters without so much as a by-your-leave, planting the Schilthorn in the proscenium box for this most marvellous of all dramatic performances. Surely this was a challenge that had to be accepted – the only question was, How?

A Shorter History of the Aerial Cableway

The monkeys have found an excellent solution to the problem of how to get where you want to be in the shortest possible time. The liana dangling between the trees in the jungle afford a means of saving a time-consuming detour through the undergrowth if the monkey wraps his legs around a bunch of them and then pulls himself along by his arms. Then came the time when man took a leaf out of his hairy predecessors' book and started using cables as a means of transport. For even the Red Indian uses this most basic of all bridges for crossing narrow gorges and rushing waters when stalking his quarry. However, given that the art of twining strong ropes from plant fibres and strips of leather had been mastered – as already far earlier by the oriental civilizations – the step to applying this technique to towering rocks and wide rivers in deeply cleft mountain regions was not a very big one. Old

1889. Leonardo Torres' patent in Madrid for a tourist cable railway. Lateral view. Twelve parallel continuous cables lead through a steel framework with a point of embarcation. Here, too, is the steam engine with its belt drive and the tensioning appliance. The cabin runs on the twelve cables with the twelve spoked wheels all lying parallel.

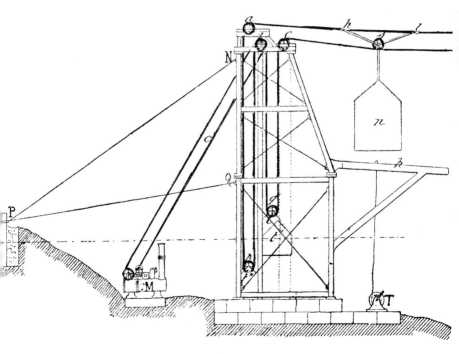

P = stabilization   M = motor   t = counterweight   T = cable winch for the platform

drawings show how the Japanese, Chinese and Indians knew how to use towlines for hoisting wooden seats or woven baskets over difficult terrain. And the ferrymen were not ignorant of the advantages afforded by the fact that the weight of the descending "vehicle" counterbalanced that of the ascending one and rollers helped them to glide more easily.

The aerial cableway is not such a recent invention as we potential moon travellers believe. The breakthrough into the third dimension was no new thing and we are given food for thought when we learn exactly where the idea of this form of transport progressed fastest in Europe – as usual, on the warpath. This device proved invaluable when making entrenchments and bulwarks from great masses of earth and building materials and for positioning the horses and their riders, the heavy cannon and cannon-balls. In

▶ *The Schilthorn and its main rail and road approach routes from the north-east, north-west and south. The map shows the tectonic structure of the region which lies in the seam between the old crystalline mountain massif and the younger elevations of the Helvetic stratum and owes its unique beauty to the resulting diversity of terrain features.*
▼ *The four sections of the Schilthorn Cableway, stations and lengths of line. The layout corresponds to the aerial photograph on pp. 120/121. The main technical specifications are given on p. 26.*

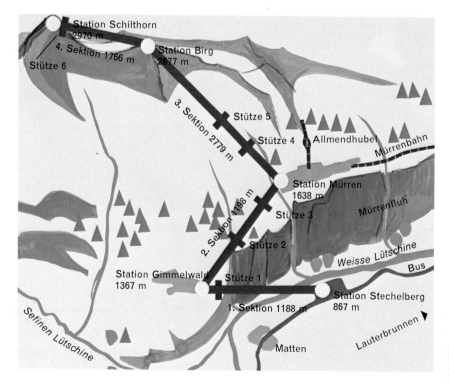

1405, the author of a popular manual on military strategy wrote as follows – albeit with suitably Spartan brevity – in his instructions for building a "cable railway" across an obstructing watercourse, "Useful work of engineering for transporting horseriders. Observe and consider what, how many, who, how and when… If required, the rope can be pulled back by a thin cord" (Keyser von Eichstädt, "Bellifortis"). The functioning of that old work of engineering must have seemed every bit as audacious and mysterious to the Europe of 600 years ago as that of the first space vessels appeared to the whole world in 1969. But the cable railway had nonetheless made its début and even in the 15th century there were several recipes for building it. One method in particular was used in which the continuous traction cable also served as carrier cable (the system used today for chair- and ski-lifts) with a number of containers attached to it at regular intervals. There was also an arrangement using separate traction and carrier cables (the to-and-fro system used in the aerial ropeway) with at most two containers.

Cast iron was introduced in this context by Messrs. Joh. Jakob Rieter & Co. of the Töss Valley – near Schaffhausen in 1866. They smuggled a little 101-metre cableway into the power transmission plant of the waterworks on the Rhine whose fame had spread beyond the frontiers of Europe. A little wagon, carefully operated by a hand crank, shuttled back and forth

1897. A Swiss invention affording the proverbial safety. The passenger cabin is coccooned in three dozen cables stretched between the mountain and the valley. There are guide rollers above, below and at the sides of the cabin. There are no intermediate masts. The idea came from Mr. A. Margesin of Zurich.

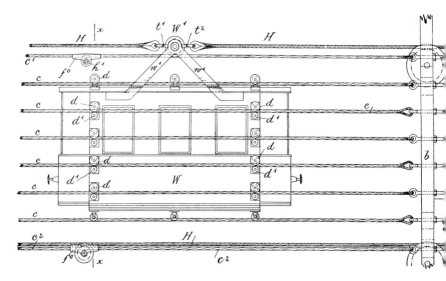

across the river along the ropes of the great cable transmission installation, carrying the technicians. Two extra pairs of carrier cables laid one above the other, 160 cm apart, served as rails, running over sheaves at either end to regulate the length and tension. The four rollers at each side of the wagon all had a little counter-roller to prevent derailing.

It is possible that Europe's original passenger lift was not far from this first cable railway. In the eighteen-sixties another storey had been added to the elegant and exclusive Weber Hotel above the falls of the Rhine at Schaffhausen. In order to save the guests a wearisome climb up the stairs after their post-prandial constitution, they were provided with the convenience of being carried upstairs in a cabin raised by a cable! Both hotel and cable transmission have disappeared but it is interesting to discover how cables came to be so fashionable in Schaffhausen a hundred years ago.

During his travels in Germany, in Hanoverian Clausthal, a young man called Carl Caspar Oechslin immediately saw the possibilities in the stranded metal rope invented by the mining engineer, Albert. In 1860 he lost no time in commencing production of these new ropes in his father's hempen-rope factory near Schaffhausen on the Rhine. The enterprise acquired an international reputation by supplying the material for rope transmissions which were widely used at that time for power transmission.

It is true that the aerial cableway, like the railway, developed into a means of mass transport a long way from romantic scenery and pleasure-seeking – namely, in the mining sector. The aerial cableway was designed for freight. Furthermore, the "how many, what, who and when" were all carefully specified. It was to be used for easily dividable goods in medium-sized packages, for mines and factories, in local traffic or over longer distances, in light wagons suspended on a free-hanging ropeway over crests and gulleys, fields and forests, by day and by night. The engineers in the aspiring industrial countries went to work with a will when it came to making cableways to measure in order to transport the raw materials obtained in the mines to the factories by the safest and most economical means. With the invention of the modern stranded rope (in Germany in 1834) and the locked coil rope (in England in 1884), together with its industrial production and the development of machine technology in general, the cable railway made astronomic advances in the mining sector in both the Old and the New Worlds.

The silver mine in Clear Creek County in Colorado, USA, had one of the first cable railways built on the principle of the self-acting incline with two carrier cables, intermediate supports and to-and-fro drive, i.e. two cabins linked via a rope and a deflection sheave. When one of the wagons stood at the loading ramp, the other was at the unloading end. G. W. Cypher put the cable railway into operation in 1868 and very soon repeated this performance in several variations. One of his models used two parallel carrier cables as rails and a machine-driven endless traction cable allowing the wagons to travel one behind the other. The layout, later known as the "German system", was thoroughly studied in all its detail during the eighteen-seventies, particularly by Adolf Bleichert and Th. Otto in Leipzig. Not long afterwards, dozens of similar installations went into operation in Europe and overseas.

The "English system" was an improvement by Charles Hodgson on an already existing system, parts of which were patented in 1868; this had only one cable, a continuous one supported at intermediate points by posts or chock-type supports, which carried the wagons along with it. The prototype, kept in motion by a willing horse, was in Richmond. The single-rope "English system" – later steam-driven – was suitable for use in places where the loads were light and the terrain gently sloping; the construction

The hollow between Allmendhubel and Birg, popularly known as the Blumental because of its magnificent flora; the cables of the Schilthorn Cableway stretching up to Birg are barely visible here. During the eighteen-nineties, the "environmentalists" already started worrying about the slashing of the mountain slopes by the rails of the funiculars.

costs were in general rather less than in the case of the sturdier "German" installation. But the question had to be carefully examined whether to use one rope which was necessarily subject to greater wear and tear, or if it would be better to divide the traction and the load between two or more ropes.

All the combinations described above offered enormous scope to engineers of all disciplines long before the turn of the century and prior to the introduction of electrical drive. It was now up to them to study the details and make good the deficiencies as they became apparent. It was the engineer's job to attend to things like the saddle to take the rope through the supports, the support rollers for the traction cable and the design and material of the masts. A particularly delicate question concerned the coupling of the carrier cable and the splicing of the traction cable. One needs to be in God's good books when casting cable couplings! Then there was the

A walk to Gimmeln takes you towards Schiltalp and a view of the southern slopes of the Schilthorn (left) and Birg (right). At the centre is the Seelifuhre saddle. The fourth section of the Schilthorn Cableway swings the passengers from elevation to elevation on a flight behind the scenes of the highest peaks – all included in the fare!

matter of the sag in the cable and the distribution of tension. There were endless parabolic computations to be made and no computer to make them – and still nothing has been said about the construction of the cabins, the suspension tackle, the running gear, the rope sheave drive or the upper cable-head and the intermediate stations. The ball bounced back and forth and patents rained thick and fast.

Yet there was still no cableway for touristic purposes. These came only very gradually and with no special concessions being made to the "human freight". It took a full twenty years to achieve the step from the technicians' cableway across the Rhine at Schaffhausen to the suspension ferry over the Teremakay River near Blackpool in New Zealand which attracted such

1902. Mr. Feldmann, an engineer from Elberfeld, introduced his invention for a tourist cableway using two carrier cables, one above the other, and two traction cables. A number of projects used this system during the years that followed; among other things, it was planned to build a free-swinging ropeway up to the Eiger peak from the Eismeer Station, opened in 1905 on the Jungfrau Railway then under construction. This picture was among the documents submitted in support of the application for a licence. But the Eiger cableway never got off the ground.

worldwide interest. But the latter did not look all that different from the former. It was twice as long, it is true, and it had two carrier cables and a continuous traction cable driven by a steam winch. It remained in operation without accident for eleven years until it was relieved by a permanent bridge.

It was high time now for the cableway to be used elsewhere than at the water's edge, and things seemed to be happening around Mount Pilatus and on the Eiger and the Wetterhorn.

►► *The upper terminus of the Stock cableway that it was planned to build on the Gemmi Pass in 1909 (see also below), with the anchorage of the carrier cables, the electromotor drive and the deflection sheaves of the traction cable (centre) which carried an idle arrester cable when a coupling was engaged on the main axle. If the traction cable snapped the voltage was taken over by the arrester cable drive and the entire installation simultaneously stopped. The auxiliary drive facility had a reserve motor. A hydraulic brake regulator driven from the main shaft ensured that the cableway ran at a regular speed. If the tension on the traction cable reached a certain maximum or minimum value, the brake current was automatically switched off and the cableway brought to an immediate standstill.*

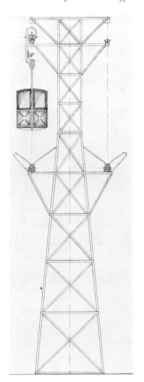

From 1908 to 1911 various groups with common interests sought to bridge the Gemmi Pass with the aid of aerial ropeways. The application for a concession submitted by Alfred Hurter in Zurich envisaged an aerial cableway from Kandersteg to Stock, with two parallel carrier cables, side by side, along which two cabins were to be drawn in opposite directions by a cable, similar to the funicular railways on rails. The running gear of a cabin was equipped with twelve rollers, three sitting on each of four axles. The eight outer rollers carried the cabin during the journey on the carrier cables; the four inner rollers took it over the supports on special bearings. The nine masts required (see picture) had special rotary cable shoes where the middle running gear rollers passed over a slightly raised rib between the two carrier cable ring guides so that the outer rollers did not touch the carrier cables during the crossover. At the centre of the picture are the bearing rollers for the traction cable and the idle arrester cable it carries. The Gemmi railways planned at that time for transit traffic were soon submerged by the vast project for a Lötschberg railway.

35

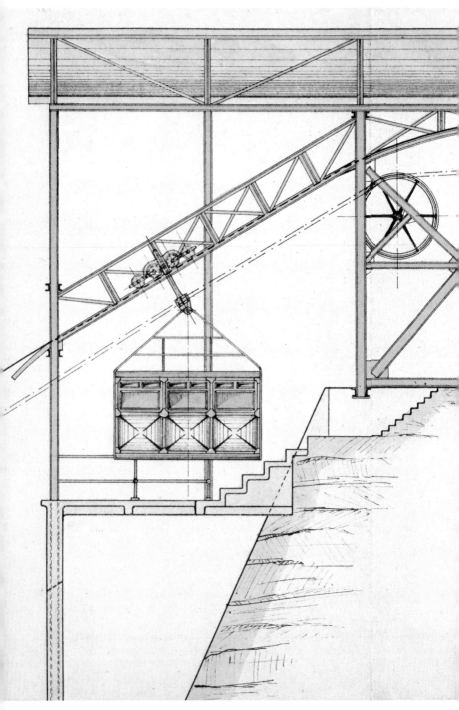

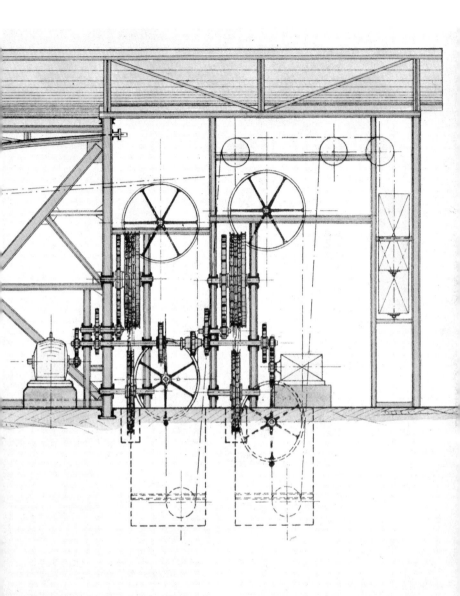

37

Balancing Act

What was needed was an alpine-type aerial cableway, rather like the people in those regions – robust and reliable, lively even, but always with its feet planted solidly on the ground. Could the melting-pot of all those systems produce something appropriate?

Yes, indeed! After all, the aerial ropeway was at home in the mountains, doing duty for the pathway where mule and waggon could no longer pass. The story of the cable railway is full of surprises: there is the Cordillera Railway in the Argentine, built in 1904 to exploit the copper mines at Mont Blanc height. This 34 km long cableway covers a total ascent of 3400 m and has eight sections all hooked together; the cable hangs free over distances of up to 800 m; there are 275 supports up to 50 m high, tunnels and a varied assortment of "rolling stock". The copper ore that it previously took a year to carry by packhorse along narrow sumpter paths from the mountain to the valley, was transported by the cable railway in four days. With no regard whatever for the topographical avarice of the region, the giant ropeways ate their way straight as an arrow up the mountainside or lolloped fleet as hares

through jungle and desert, over deep gorges, steep slopes and high peaks, going from strength to strength, in the Siebenrichter Forest or the coal-seams of Peking, in Serbia or the Volga Woods or in the Usambara Mountains in Africa. They were sometimes as long as 80 km, with gradients of as much as 1:1.2 and built to carry the heaviest loads. What, then, was to prevent the aerial ropeway from making a beeline up the Eiger Wall? The answer to that – if the truth be told – is, red tape and a sinking feeling in the pit of the general public's stomach.

The Swiss Federal Council sat vigilantly at the controls. In Autumn 1903 a lengthy document landed on the Federal Councillors' desk – an application for permission to build a mountain railway on the Wetterhorn (the application was filed on 14th October 1903 by Feldmann and Stoessel for the construction of an aerial ropeway from the Wetterhorn Hotel at the foot of the Upper Grindelwald glacier to the Gleckstein Clubhouse 1100 m higher up). If, by any chance, the Council and the people were not already acquainted with the convincing characteristics of the aerial cableway, they were now instructed on the subject with a vengeance. "The mountain lift," proclaimed the supporting documents, "is capable of climbing even the steepest and most inaccessible peaks – peaks which can at present be reached by only a select few who have the necessary strength and training and who are lacking neither in courage and a sense of enterprise, nor in the necessary funds and the time to await a favourable opportunity – and even then they need first-class guides and several days for the expedition." Even when all these conditions were fulfilled, argued the applicants, tours of this kind would always involve very considerable risks and require great human sacrifice and a whole series of fine days. On the other hand, mountain lifts would allow even the untrained tourist to take quick advantage of a few hours of sunshine. Even when there is fog, the trip to the peak would often be worthwhile as fog is seldom so unrelievedly dense that a sudden lifting is

In 1908 the first aerial cableway in Switzerland, licensed in 1904, went into operation: this linked Grindelwald with Engi Station on the Wetterhorn and was intended to be the first section of a lift up to the peak. Based on the Feldmann system, the traction and carrier cables – as described on pp. 44–48 – were completely surrounded by the brake van and the cabin. The ropeway operated perfectly. The firm that built the Wetterhorn ropeway, Von Roll, was to build the Schilthorn Cableway 60 years later – the longest tourist aerial cableway in the world.

▶ ▶ Eiger, Mönch and Jungfrau seen from the terrace on the Schilthorn peak – that massive triumvirate whose magnetic attraction is felt far across the plain. Small wonder that this radiant constellation, along with the Matterhorn, already had mountain railway pioneers dreaming dreams of conquest during the last century. People and parliament waxed enthusiastic about the half-baked projects for graduated ropeways and mountain lifts on rails up to the highest peaks – and are still talking about them today.

altogether precluded. And, after all, was not precisely the movement of the clouds against the mountain slopes or the view from clear heights upon the billowing blanket of fog below a very special attraction? The view from the peak was not the only reason why people went on alpine tours, the argument continued; the other pleasures, such as the pure air and the satisfaction of overcoming danger, were also not to be under-estimated; and one of the main fascinations when climbing a mountain was surely the ever-changing landscape and the awe-inspiring might of the rock masses, gorges and deeply cleft glaciers. Is it not generally accepted that it is precisely the view from halfway up the mountain which is usually far more magnificent than the prospect from the highest elevation? And it is just this halfway view which is so happily afforded from the free-hanging cabin of an aerial ropeway. The pleasure experienced in overcoming danger would, of course, have to give place to the satisfaction of having avoided risks.

In short, continued Messrs. Feldmann and Stoessel, the Jungfrau Railway – whose completion was called in question at that time – could be helped upwards by a mountain lift from the planned Eismeer Station to the Eiger peak (illustration of this project on p. 34). The steeper the peaks and the rock faces were, the more easily would they be mastered by a mountain lift. One had only to look at the Matterhorn – six sections would cope with it easily. However, before constructing mountain lifts at heights of this kind, it might – they thought – be a good idea to erect smaller installations at lower altitudes in order, on the one hand, to gain the confidence of the public and the financial world and, on the other, to collect experience regarding the icing of the cable. The best opportunity for this would appear to be afforded by the Wetterhorn. Not only did the steep, smooth, solid walls of the mountain foot promise an outstandingly safe installation, but the flower-studded green of the broad Gleckstein meadows, accessible by two sections of ropeway, also afforded the most marvellous view of the glaciers. A mountain health resort could be built here, with gentle walks through soft meadows and the opportunity to indulge in safe climbing and to pick the edelweiss. Moreover, there was nothing to prevent a continuation of the ropeway up to the peak: the third ropeway for the western ridge, spanning 455 m, could be reached by an invigorating, gallery-punctuated traverse across the Stotzweng on the northern side of the mountain, and another walk past a succession of ever-changing views would lead to the fourth lift stretching the last 800 m up the southern flank to the peak.

Moreover, the applicants had reached prior agreement with, firstly, the mountain communities of Grindel and Scheidegg concerning replacement of the Gleckstein Clubhouse by a hotel, already under construction; secondly, with the Jungfrau Railway which was to supervise the building and operating of the ropeway; and, thirdly, with the local authorities in Grindelwald who were to supply the necessary electricity. A test cable had already been hung down the rock face and Mr. Feldmann, the engineer, was waiting in the Jolimont Pension in Berne for the Federal Council to reach a decision. Mr. Feldmann came from Elberfeld in Prussia and had conceived his "highflown" plans while supervising construction of the Barmen-Elberfeld suspension railway. Anyone requiring information about Dr. Stoessel could obtain it from the Ministry of Finance in the Kingdom of Saxony.

The cable on the Wetterhorn had all the time in the world to prove itself in all kinds of weather; not so the originator of the project. Even if a provisional building licence had been drafted by the railways department of the Swiss Federal Ministry of Transport and Communications, final permission to build the ropeway to the Gleckstein Hotel was granted only in March 1907. The first section of the ropeway up to Engi went into operation in July 1908 – at almost the same time as the first Kohlerer cable railway near Bozen. But unhappily Mr. Feldmann did not live to see the day.

The aerial cableway had caught the Swiss confederates on the wrong foot. The law governing the railways – which was introduced in 1872 and left the construction of railways to private initiative while entrusting supervision to the Confederation – had led them to expect they would be dealing with rolling stock and not pendulating cabins. The Federal Council gave the aerial ropeway pioneers to understand that it would be difficult to find a means of applying the railway law to this newfangled vehicle and that they would do better to consult the cantons and the local authorities. Among these troublesome innovators were Masson, who applied in January 1888

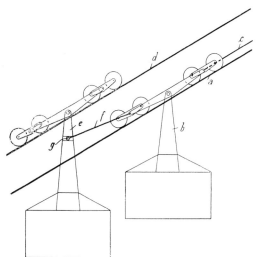

1910. Before the aerial cableway had gained a proper footing in the mountains, devices to increase its capacity were already being thought up. There was the patent of Adolf Bleichert & Co. in Leipzig-Gohlis. Several carrier cables were laid one above the other as a track for the cabins, whereby only one car was directly attached to the traction cable, the others being just carried along. As required, a cabin was coupled to the "leader" by a rod f which gripped a bolt g.

for permission to build an electric cable bridge from Waisenhausplatz across the River Aare in Berne; Küenzi, who asked in February 1888 to be allowed to build a cable lift from the River Aare up to the cathedral platform in Berne; and Torres y Quevedo, Santander, who sent in his application in March 1889 concerning the pendulating omnibus on Mount Pilatus.

But the tinder had been kindled. How, now, was a deluge of applications from rival cantons to be forestalled and control of the new invention obtained by the Confederation? There was, of course, the post monopoly which made all regular and passenger transport undertaken on a commercial basis a matter of Federal competence, in so far as it was not governed by some other law; so they started by issuing a Federal Decree on 14th October 1902 concerning "the control of aerial cableways and other motor-driven transport installations." But the Federal Council later decided to have its say about whether a means of passenger transport à la Wetterhorn lift might be built or not. Thus, on 18th September 1906, the categoric, parallel decree concerning "the granting of licences and the control of automobile enterprises, lifts and aerial cableways" was issued and is still valid today.

Torres y Quevedo installed his pendulating omnibus at the resort of San Sebastian on the Bay of Biscay in 1907, thus presenting his country with what was probably the first tourist ropeway in Europe. It had a span of 280 m and an ascent of 28 m, with an electric motor to drive the traction cable. To quieten the anxieties of the public, the open gondola ran on six carrier cables (see patent on p. 27).

The feature which distinguished Mr. Feldmann's mountain lift from all previous steep transport installations was the care that had been lavished on the safety precautions and it was this that ultimately convinced the experts. The two cabins were suspended by two traction cables wound two-and-a-half times around horizontal driving wheels in the upper terminus. The two cables on both tracks were so attached to the cabins by a triangular girder that changes of tension in one cable were immediately compensated by a similar change in the other and any slackening – such as a break in a cable – triggered the safety brake. Ludwig von Roll's ironworks in Berne, which had already become reliably specialized in mountain railway construction (it was Von Roll who later on built the Schilthorn cableway),

The western slopes of the Lauterbrunnen Valley and particularly the windless bowl of the Sefinen Valley below the Schilthorn are noted for their infinitely varied flora. If you're passing that way, don't let them tempt you, for each flower picked – and it is usually the strongest – impairs the chances of its kind in the competition for the best location against its unplucked neighbour. This is why it is forbidden by law to pick the yellow wolf's-bane and many other alpine flowers.

undertook to draft and execute all the mechanical installations, including the cabins, the drive and the cable suspension (see picture on p. 38). Being no novices at the game, they designed an appropriate safety brake which acted on the carrier cable. This brake consisted of four wedge-shaped jaws which clamped themselves on to the running cable as soon as uneven tension in the traction cables caused a lever to trigger the tensed brake spring. In order to overcome any loss of spring tension that had occurred *en route,* a second and even stronger helical spring, triggered simultaneously by a latch mechanism, shot a locking device into the brake jaws and the cabin hung totally immobilized on the carrier cables. In order to refloat the cabin, so to speak, the conductor had to climb up a little stairway on to the roof. The functioning of this device was not unlike that of today's multi-step automatic brake (running van of the Schilthorn cabin on p. 79). But apart from this, almost all the safety measures required today were already exploited at that time: the hand-brake in the cabin, auxiliary winching gear with two emergency cabins, auxiliary motors and hand winches in case of a power failure, a hand-brake and an automatic safety brake on the driving shaft of the main motor – a brake which was activated in the case of excessive or inadequate speed, a breakdown in the power supply, the motor or the driving gear, by the engine operator himself or if the cabin stopped too late on entering the terminus. The stations were linked by telephone and the conductor could signal from mid-air by means of a horn.

For each cabin on the Wetterhorn lift, two carrier cables of locked coil design were spanned, but one above the other instead of side by side. Through leverage on the free-hanging counterweight anchored in the lower

The railway lines in the Bernese Oberland obediently followed the growing stream of tourists. In 1857 the Winteregg alpine co-operative in Mürren had already built a first modest hotel, the Silberhorn, leasing it to the Sterchi family who ran a summer boardinghouse in Unterseen.

◄◄ Mürren circa 1920. While the hamlet nestles in the hollow in the foreground to the right, the big hotels are lording it over the lush fields. – Eiger, Mönch, Schwarzmönch.

terminus – which was the important feature in Feldmann's patent – constant compensation of length and tension in the cables was so achieved via flat link articulated chains that the cabins remained immobilized in a balanced position even if the load were lopsided, or in the highly unlikely event of a break in the cable. The unique construction of the brake van, which completely surrounded the carrier cables, was permitted by the absence of intermediate supports. This was also why the steepest rock faces were best suited to this type of lift.

The Wetterhorn lift was regarded as a trial run. All other building projects for aerial cableways were held back by the authorities until it had been satisfactorily proved that these revolutionary installations harboured no fatal flaw. The lift functioned beautifully, but it ended on a strip of rock that fell steeply away. Only the second section would have reached the Gleckstein meadows. After years of war and crisis, during which the lift was neither operated nor maintained, the installation was dismantled in 1934. (Table showing the first aerial cableways on p. 113).

Unspoilt Nature in Mürren. The white tip of the Ebnefluh gleams over the Rottal Glacier surging out of its inhospitable abyss. The tales of love and despair told by Lauterbrunnen legend centre on the Rottal.

Fresh Alpine Milk

It's a special day today. From the branches of fir-tree and rowan, the clear-voiced chaffinches and all our other feathered friends are madly tuning up: chirping and trilling, whistling and chattering, fluting and jubilating. There are larks, pipits and fallow-finches, the inquisitive coal tits, the wood warbler, the kitty wren and the hedge-sparrow, with the black woodpecker beating time. What a glorious spring! Get up, lazybones – the day is dawning! There, over the dark collar of the Black Monk's cape, the first hint of a new day glimmers, then wanders softly and silently, clad in rosy mystery, from the Tschingelhorn to the Breithorn. And now the sun is shining in earnest, bidding the flowers good morning as they nod and curtsey – the bluebells and the white lilies, the yellow- and orange-fringed baskets of the hawkweed, the clover and the wild orchid, the lilac-coloured scabious and the bright-eyed pinks. Just smell that air – a heady mixture of resin, earth

Anyone at home? – The whole family is doubtless haymaking on the nearby slopes, young and old all lending a hand. The houses in Mürren and Gimmelwald remind one of the Valais – and so they should for they are old Walser settlements.

The staff of the Hôtel des Alpes in Mürren take a moment off from looking after the fashion-able guests to pose for a commemorative photograph in front of the house. In 1885 the hotel had just about everything likely to attract guests from Europe and abroad, including an alpine dairy farm, a nursery with greenhouses and its very own electric powerhouse!
▶ *The Blue Salon at the Grand Hôtel des Alpes. Aristocratic ladies and other hothouse plants were borne in sedans up to the health resort.*

and the scent of flowers, with the merest suggestion of fresh coffee and crisply-baked rolls added by the gentle breeze. Where shall this bright new day take us? Through the steaming woods and richly-jewelled fields, or steeply upwards, over narrow footpaths, scree and sward, to the gentians, the wild primulas and the soldanella – and past the few remaining shields of fast-disappearing snow? The inner man brings us down to earth again – an army marches on its stomach!

Mürren has a gastronomic tradition. In the middle of the 19th century the alpine co-operative of Winteregg plucked up the courage to step out of its auxiliary rôle of modest caravanserai with beds of hay and menus of milk and soup and, in 1857, to build the Silberhorn Hotel on the outskirts of the sun-bronzed village of Mürren – perhaps the village fathers were concerned for the virtue of the village maidens. The Silberhorn offered real beds and a more varied menu within well-carpentered walls. Johann Sterchi from

50

51

Matten was made responsible for the welfare of the guests. "Everything spick and span in kitchen and cellar despite the proximity of the heavens," reported those passing through, whose destination was invariably the Schilthorn, but who had nothing against a brief sojourn in the sunwashed village of Mürren. Mr. Sterchi, who later became a member of parliament, bought a parcel of land below the Silberhorn where he built the Mürren Hotel in 1870. He then added a wing, bought up the Silberhorn and entrusted its management in 1879 to his son-in-law, Joseph Müller from Gersau. Subsequently, a four-storey tract was inserted between the two buildings, with a dining-room on the ground floor. A kursaal was added, the rooms were dressed in silks and satins and equipped with what later became known as "all mod. cons." Under the name of the Mürren Grand Hotel and Kurhaus, with 250 beds, the establishment acquired a praiseworthy single star (Munich and Pils beers!) in Karl Baedecker's Guide at the turn of the century and became a haunt of Europe's *haute volée*. (See p. 53).

But there were others who were not letting the grass – or the flowers – grow under their feet. Right next door were Mr. Sterchi's competitors – the Jungfrau, Eiger, Alpenruhe, Beausite, Belmont and Edelweiss hotels, the Blumental Pension and Zum Sternen Inn, with 330 beds between them, while the Grand Hôtel des Alpes offered accommodation for a further 170 guests and also had a star in the Guide – but a different kind of beer, Münchner Spatenbräu. In this establishment, Wilhelm Gurtner loaded his tables with all the good things dearest to the gourmet's heart – noble wines from his own cellar, strawberries from his own gardens, clotted cream from his own alpine dairy farm and meat from his own slaughterhouse. Fresh crabs came from the coast and the fine porcelain came from Dresden. The hotelier's young wife found constant use for the first-aid box she had got a doctor to equip and explain to her (the village had no doctor of its own), as not a day passed but one of the tightly-laced, wasp-waisted lady guests had an attack of the vapours after one of Mr. Gurtner's mammoth meals. The polyglot conversation of the guests vied with the chirping of the birds in the trees around the hotel – nor were the guests themselves any less varied and colourful than their feathered rivals. One met Conrad Ferdinand Meyer – "Do you know Mürren? Unforgettable!" –, Ferdinand Hodler, whose picture of the Jungfrau you have doubtless seen, Spelterini the balloonist, Richard Strauss, Roland Bonaparte, Joseph Chamberlain the British statesman, Princess Mary, heiress to the British throne, Henry Morton Stanley, just back from Africa and the hero of a young generation – all in all, a happy mixture of nationalities. They fluttered off in the morning and came home to roost every evening. It was Christian Gurtner, proprietor of the Steinbock Inn at Lauterbrunnen, who, in 1870, had bought the flower-

The old Silberhorn, promoted to "Grand Hôtel Kurhaus Mürren", despatched its own luggage-boy on rails to meet the guests at the new railway station on the Mürren wall. "The passenger fare is 30 centimes, the speed to be stipulated by the Federal Council", says the licence of 13th April 1894. The trolley had a gauge of 50 cm and was trundled along the 450 m stretch by a horse or a hotel porter.

jewelled fields above the Silberhorn Hotel and had built the Grand Hôtel des Alpes there, putting it into the hands of his son, Wilhelm, in 1879 (see pictures on pp. 50/51).

The Bernese poet, Johann Viktor Widmann, once asked that the hotels break with the tradition of the communal table, giving the guests small, individual tables instead; he felt himself daunted by the self-assured Britons! But it was precisely the English who discovered the revitalizing powers of the winter sun, who sought opportunities for sport amidst the snow and who consequently headed the list of those filling the hotels in winter as well. Up till then the Mürren hotels had closed after the last golden days of autumn. The enterprising owner of the Hôtel des Alpes was the first to prolong the season and to invite his guests to engage in winter sports at Christmas in 1903. He made a skating-rink and laid down a toboggan-run, leaving the open slopes to extend their own invitation to the skiers. The rooms were centrally-heated. A winter fairytale in brilliant sunshine and crisp, white snow awaited the guests. The only thing lacking was a suitable mode of transport. On arrival, the guests were met in the valley by porters with horses and had to find their way up to Mürren along the sumpter path kept open during the difficult winter months by the hotelier himself. The Mürren Railway, which had opened in 1891, functioned only from May to October.

During the winter the railway refused to operate, fighting shy of the expensive construction of two avalanche shelters, non-stop snow removal and the installation of steps affording access to the line on the funicular stretch of the railway between Grütschalp and Lauterbrunnen. What was more, the railway-owned power station on the Staubbach failed to supply sufficient electricity in the winter and the source of the Jungfrau Railway had to be tapped. The authorities would not permit the Mürren Railway to run unless all the required conditions were fulfilled. – "We are unable to decide in favour of introducing winter operations, especially since Mürren is in no way suitable as a winter-sports resort." This was the excuse offered by the Mürren Railway, staunchly seconded by the hotelier who preferred to serve his Munich and Pils beer during the warmer season. This was understandable as he owned railway shares and had an establishment that was difficult to heat.

The highlight of any visit to Mürren was always a trip up the Schilthorn. Saddle-horses and sedan chairs lent the outing the appearance of an expedition. To reach the peak by sunrise, the night was spent in the Schilthorn Hut below the upper slope. On reaching the cross at the summit, everyone shook hands and thanked the guide.

◄◄ *The old Schilthorn Hut above the Grauseeli. The gold of the Ebnefluh reflected in the little lake in the last evening light augured well for the morrow. The new and more comfortable Schilthorn Hut belonging to the Mürren Skiing Club is situated at the mouth of the Engital.*

The Mürren hoteliers, jealous of the chamois on the Wetterhorn and put out at having their business activities thus curtailed, decided that what they needed was one of those lightning cableways like the one in Grindelwald. The proprietors of the Mürren hotels had followed the first winter experiment with interest and been forced to concede that it simply would not work without a railway link. The man responsible for the experiment had been strong as a horse at the beginning of the season and dead from an illness following exhaustion and heartbreak at the end of it. It was Fritz von Allmen, owner of the Edelweiss on the outer margin of the rock wall, who also recognized the fascination of skiing as a sport and on 7th August 1906 took it upon himself to write to the Ministry of Transport and Communications in Berne, thus making the first move in hewing a pendulating railway out of the Mürren wall. "The majority of the hotel proprietors in Mürren plan to keep their establishments open for the winter season," he wrote; "to these

►► *An autumn morning on the Schilthorn – what more can the heart desire? There, where the endless distance begins, the mountains of the Entlebuch and the Lake of Lucerne – Schrattenfluh, Schafmatt, Pilatus, Rigi – gaze down into the elongated trough of the Lake of Brienz. Dead centre is the Schynige Platte with the Saustal in the foreground, upon whose green plains in the dim and distant past a village is said to have existed 2000 m up where the cowherds' hut now stands. Schwarzbirg and Bietenlücke lie in violet shadow.*

ends, some form of transport is necessary. Keeping the Mürren Railway open is too expensive an undertaking. The Mürren hoteliers therefore plan as follows: 1. To instal an aerial cableway from Stegmatten near Trümmelbach up to Mürren. 2. To instal an aerial cableway from Stegmatten up to Trümmletenbachtal and thence to establish an adhesion railway link with Wengernalp Station." Mr. von Allmen politely enquired whether there was anything in the existing railway concessions of the Mürren and Wengernalp Railways which might be construed as an obstacle to this plan.

Nobody at the Ministry had anything against Point 1 if the Mürren Railway persisted in refusing to introduce winter operations. Mr. von Allmen should be good enough to submit the documents required to support an application for a licence: technical report, site plan, layout plan and longitudinal profile. However, no real need could be seen for Point 2, replied the man from the Ministry. He obviously had no topographical relief map in his office and was unable to picture the 800 metre-high Mürren wall. The technical advisers to the Ministry whistled him back immediately, pointing

A traction cable being hung in the third section of the Schilthorn Cableway between Mürren and Birg. 12000 m of carrier cable and 24000 m of traction cable had to be laid in November and December 1964 after completion of masts 4 and 5.

out that it would have been better "to maintain the attitude adopted towards other applications for similar concessions, i.e. to refuse any further licences for the construction of aerial cableways until experience has been obtained of the system at present being tested in Grindelwald." But as the man from the Ministry had already placed matters on a somewhat different footing, the technical advisers were prepared to let things stand so long as a clause

Carrier cable supports and anchoring stations on the Schilthorn Cableway

Stretch	Mast No.	Height of mast	Counterweight shaft in	Depth	Anchor bollard in
1st section	1	18 m	Stechelberg	7.2 m	Gimmelwald
2nd section	2	41 m	Mürren	25.0 m	Gimmelwald
	3	27 m			
3rd section	4	45 m	Mürren	25.0 m	Birg
	5	26 m			
4th section	6	13 m	Birg	21.4 m	Schilthorn

The various building sites were made accessible by erection ropeways. While the Stechelberg–Mürren stretch, which overcame the wall at one fell swoop, is still running (picture on pp. 88/89), the other erection ropeways and their 24 masts have been dismantled.

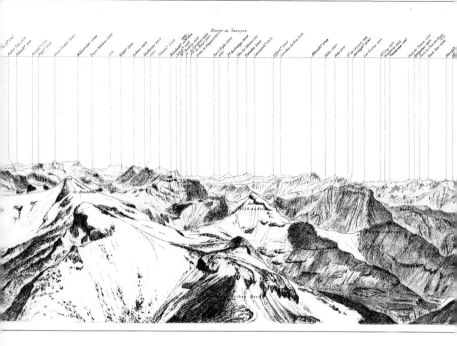

were added to the concession as a "safety brake." The correspondence continued for years – first the plans, then the decision, said the Ministry in Berne. But studies and plans cost money, so the hotel proprietors in Mürren politely insisted on being given a reply to their basic question first.

It is entirely due to a felicitous coincidence that the dispute is not still continuing today. In August 1907 a letter from a certain Dr. Henry S. Lunn reached the Hôtel des Alpes in Mürren, enquiring whether the hotel was to remain open during the following winter. They would have heard about his travel agency, continued the letter, and the winter clientèle was growing so rapidly that Dr. Lunn was in need of fresh resorts. It would, however, be pointless to consider Mürren so long as there were no railway link. The Mürren Railway woke up with a bump: that being the case, they said, winter operations could perhaps be considered if the local tourist administration committee were prepared to guarantee the operating costs and the interest on any monies required for alterations. "Propaganda takes time – what is needed now is the assurance of winter rail operations or a concession for the immediate construction of an aerial cableway." The administrative committee took a firm stand and in winter of 1910/11 Mürren had its all-the-year-round railway link. Even the Kurhaus girded itself for a winter season. Fine, said the guests; what we want now – and quickly! – is a sports

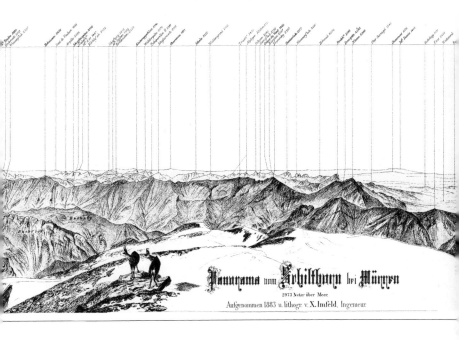

Panorama vom Schilthorn bei Mürren
2973 Meter über Meer.
Aufgenommen 1883 u. lithogr. v. X. Imfeld, Ingenieur.

As a young man, Xaver Imfeld, the engineer from Obwalden, was already famous as a pastmaster of relievo (his works can be seen at the Alpine Museums of Berne and Munich). In 1883 his contemporary, mine host at the Grand Hôtel des Alpes, brought Xaver to Mürren to draw the Schilthorn panorama. Wilhelm Gurtner had the blue-hatched prospect carefully printed and used it from then on (all 320 cm of it!) as propaganda for his flourishing establishment.

lift. In October 1911 an application was filed for permission to construct an electrical funicular from Mürren up to the Allmendhubel; the building licence was granted in December and a year later the railway was already finished (concession: Max Müller. O. Lehmann, H. Morgenthaler, for the Allmendhubel cable railway, 22nd December 1911. See p. 93.)

Mürren had got itself a goose which showed every sign of laying golden eggs. Dr. Lunn and his Alpine Sports Ltd. – a club in London for the cream of society – promptly purchased the Hôtel des Alpes, renovated and enlarged it and ran it under the anglicized name of The Palace. Mürren could now look forward to a period of hard-earned prosperity. Like St. Moritz, it became the playground of the sport-loving English aristocracy who were followed by the élite of the skiing world.

Nothing venture, nothing gain... look at things how you will. There'll be no milk from the cow unless the animal's fed.

61

Animated Suspension on the Schilthorn

Where the proprietor of the Edelweiss and his fellow-hoteliers had wanted a "winterproof" mountain lift all those years ago, a cableway really did plunge over the Mürren wall into the depths of Lauterbrunnental – the transport ropeway for the Schilthorn cableway erected a full generation later. On 28th April 1962 the Schilthorn Cableway Company was founded with registered offices in Mürren. The following year the preparatory ropeway from Stechelberg to Mürren was already running (winch-operated); two months later the Mürren–Birg transport ropeway was ready (to-and-fro system with 20 supports). After another ten months the transport ropeway reached the slopes of the Schilthorn peak (again on the to-and-fro system with two-way traffic). The Gimmelwald section was given its own ropeway so that building materials could be despatched thence. An endless stream of supplies flowed up the mountain; one by one, round the clock, the open wagons with their loads of between 1.5 and 3 tons followed each other up to the peak. The total volume carried by the Schilthorn erection ropeways would have filled a goods train stretching from Berne to Thoune, plus a passenger train carrying 28,500 people. The cables, conveyor belts and winches had the Devil on their heels, running under extreme pressure, with only a few minor disturbances right at the beginning. The Schilthorn Cableway Company operated the erection ropeway themselves to ensure that everything was available when it was required; the various contractors' freight was carried at previously agreed rates and, while the Company was

The average annual temperature on the Schilthorn peak is -4° C. Because of the permafrost the weathered, slatey substratum is interspersed with ice lentils which never thaw out, even in summer. Air spaces had to be left between the rock and the containing walls of the building to ensure heat exchange.

◄◄ *A Russian helicopter – the strongest machine available – hoisting part of the building crane up the Schilthorn.*

63

about it, they kept a weather-eye on any teething troubles that developed with a view to eliminating them in the finished article. When the Schilthorn Cableway was finally opened to the public, it was equipped with the very best and robustest that money could buy and modern technology dream up. The erection ropeways vanished from the fields and rock faces like the rash after measles; they were all dismantled with the exception of the one which led directly up the Mürren wall. This still exists and leads a quite impressive life of its own. The Devil, finding himself out of work, dived head first into the nearest bottle of kirsch and has been served up ever since on the Schilthorn in the traditional fortifier they call "inferno coffee." (See diagram of the cableway on p. 28).

While the Devil was sitting at the winches, the strategy was being bewitched. The project envisaged eleven building sites at altitudes ranging between 800 and 3000 metres, five stations and six supporting masts. Commonsense would suggest starting at the bottom and working slowly but

The Schilthorn announces the first snow at 2970 m. Not that the Schilthorn is ever snow-free! Two small glaciers have settled in the big transverse gulley and on the upper slope; these feed the Grauseeli in the hollow below. Between Birg and the Schilthorn peak, only one gondola travels to and fro with room for 100 passengers.

surely towards the top, leaving behind one building site after the other. But the witch in charge of the bewitching had other ideas – she grabbed her broomstick and took off in all four directions at once. With a flurry of skirts, she shuffled the shifts at the building sites and it became evident that she had a secret plan of her own. Above all, the third section from Mürren to Birg was to be pushed forward. With its vast span of free-hanging cable, this was the most problematical section. But once the jutting nose of the mountain was reached and made accessible by the cableway, the financial tide would turn and money start coming in for a change. Birg, at chest-level so to speak, and smack opposite the tremendous trinity of the Eiger, Mönch and Jungfrau, was a worthwhile objective for skiers and summer tourists alike, even without the possibility of continuing to the Schilthorn peak. The station at Birg was consequently equipped with a restaurant and a sun terrace. This is the ideal belvedere from which to contemplate the beauty of these three great stars of the Alps – and there was the added attraction of being able to do so from the comfort of a windscreened deck chair. The third section of the Schilthorn cableway was opened in March 1965, missing the skiing season by a hairsbreadth, while the fourth section – struggling under the triple load of the rotating restaurant that was to crown the peak, uncertain foundations and gale-force winds – had the corks popping from the champagne bottles only two years later.

The suspension of the cables over the 7000 m of the entire Schilthorn cableway was an epic in itself. It must be understood that a wire cable needs handling like fragile porcelain. Scratches, kinks, water, "candles" – that phenomenon occurring in the slack cable which is calculated to give the experts heart failure – and dirt are anathema to the sensitive cable. If it could protest it would be heard for miles around. While behaving like a mimosa, the cable is really as tough as old boots and of not inconsiderable weight – a carrier cable for Section 3 turns the scales at 26 tons (see p. 78).

Cable suspension was done from vast bobbins in Stechelberg. How? – that is undoubtedly the question that fascinates most people. First of all a thin work cable, weighted by an iron ball, was thrown down over the Mürren wall into the valley where it was drawn into the lower terminus. The thicker winch cable was then attached to it and drawn up to the upper terminus by the 20-ton winch. The heavy traction and carrier cables were then attached and pulled up in their turn. The main and auxiliary cables were always cast in the cablehead and rigidly coupled. For the time being, the cables were anchored to reinforced concrete pickets. If they were destined for a section higher up, the whole procedure began all over again.

A cable railway is always made to measure, according to the terrain and the specific requirements of the builder – there is no such thing as a pre-

▲ *The bollards that anchor the carrier cables on the Schilthorn. Each cable runs four times around the concrete drum which is clad in impregnated softwood and secured by 25 m piles; it is then stagger-shackled to a cantilever. The distance between the shackles is checked monthly to ensure there is not the least slippage. The anchorage withstands 900 tons or the equivalent of 9 express locomotives. At the lower terminus, on the Birg, the carrier cables are attached to massive concrete weights with vertical play, hung in a 21 m shaft. The ends of the cables move up and down according to the weather conditions and the load, the tension on the carrier cable and the fully loaded, moving cabins. Flexible tethers laid over big deflection sheaves are therefore inserted between the carrier cables and the weights. The grooves in the deflection sheaves holding the tethers are lined with hornbeam. In addition, the length of the stranded coil at the counterweight cable head and in the coupling sleeve is measured at two-monthly intervals.*

▶ *The most difficult building site on the Schilthorn Cableway was at the peak where work continued summer and winter as of July 1965. The basic necessities, such as a 100 kW emergency power generator, a diesel oil tank for 300–500 l daily consumption, an erection ropeway to carry 6 men, a hutment, two 7500 l water tanks, an automatic pressure pump, heatable gravel and sand silos, iron rations, telephone and radio links, the crane and a lightning protection installation with 1500 m of copper wire, ensured that building could begin.*

The compact rock expected near Mast 5 on the Schilthorn Cableway proved on excavation to be a vast, constantly creeping block resulting from an extensive primeval rockslide. The foundation had to take the form of a reinforced concrete trough which, like a ship, paralleled the movement (mere millimetres each year). The trough was also shifted 25 cm mountainwards, away from the cableway axis. This point is trigonometrically measured every two years.

▶ *Mast 5 on the Schiltgrat. At the end of the crosspiece over the 18 m long cable shoes, block and tackle can be hung so that the carrier cables on both tracks may be lifted from their guideways for inspection.*

fabricated cableway! How well everything was adapted to the Schilthorn bears witness to an infallible talent for combination that would do credit to one of the more famous couturiers. All four sections of the cableway are cut from the same cloth and the pattern used throughout is that of the fully-automatic, dual-cable aerial cableway of the to-and-fro system, i.e. there are two carrier cables for each track on which the cabins travel back and forth at the pressing of a button. But there is always one striking detail which distinguishes the creations of every artist and this is also the case here: three of the sections have only one track, but the other section – that third one – has two parallel tracks with two gondolas that cross midway. Secondly, all five cabins are held on the upward side by two traction cables, with the exception of the uppermost gondola which covers the stretch that tapers off over the Grauseeli (Little Grey Lake) and this manages with only one traction cable. Thirdly, each of stretches Nos. 3 and 4 is a completely autonomous operating unit with its own motor in the lower terminus – Birg or Mürren as the case may be. But the two lower sections have joint traction cables and together form one operating unit, with Gimmelwald as intermediate station for two homogeneous stretches. The cabins travelling out in each direction meet virtually in the middle, quickly exchange passengers and return to Stechelberg and Mürren respectively, the way they came. The

drive behind this partnership is in Mürren, i.e. in the upper terminus (see diagram on p. 71). The result of all this is that there are motors in two places only, Mürren and Birg. This simplifies the power supply – the electric and drive cables between Mürren and Birg are laid in the ground – and the maintenance, for in both places the supervisors live under the same roof as the transformers, motors and winches (see table of technical data on p. 26).

Although the overall planning of an aerial cableway including the calculations for the cables, cabins, power transmission and brakes – in short, all the mechanical installations and the entire dynamics of the project – are usually in the hands of a mechanical engineer, he will have to enlist the advice of colleagues in all branches of science and technology, such as surveyors, geologists, snow pressure and avalanche experts, even chemists, if he wants to be sure of getting the right lining for his rollers and wheels and the best lubricator for his cables. The civil engineer makes the calculations for the stations and the supports, electrical and electronics engineers attend to the drive, the regulation and the operational monitoring system. It was the geologist who conjured up the nastiest shocks on the Schilthorn; the things he brought to light from depths of 20 and 40 m in the course of his trial drilling at precisely the most sensitive points along the line of the cableway were not calculated to comfort anyone at all – moraine in Mürren, a primaeval rockslide on the Schiltgrat near Mast 5 and, right on the peak, a cap of weathered Dogger slate stone with permafrost. This spelt an awful lot of trouble. In each section of a cableway, it is customary to anchor one end of the carrier cable rigidly and the other, with a certain amount of play, in a deep shaft. The rigid attachment at the one end is made to a drum-shaped stay block whose construction serves to transmit the tensions into the ground (see picture on p. 66.) There was magnificent limestone rock at Birg and Gimmelwald stations in which to anchor the bollards – in Gimmelwald for both the upper and lower sections. There was no such thing up on the Schilthorn where the shattered rock is interspersed with great gaps and ice lentils sometimes as much as 60 cm thick. To prevent the peak itself from heading valleywards at some future date, it had to be crammed into a veritable corset of gigantic bolts in such a way that the strain resulting from the superposition of the anchoring forces was directed downwards into the nucleus of the bollard's foundation and thence into the healthy rock.

Gimmelwald Station resembles an exercise in plastic art: the horns of the two cable shoes leading into the carrier cable anchorage loom up from the unfaced deflection station of Sections 1 and 2 of the Schilthorn Cableway. In the foreground are the deflection sheaves for the traction cables.

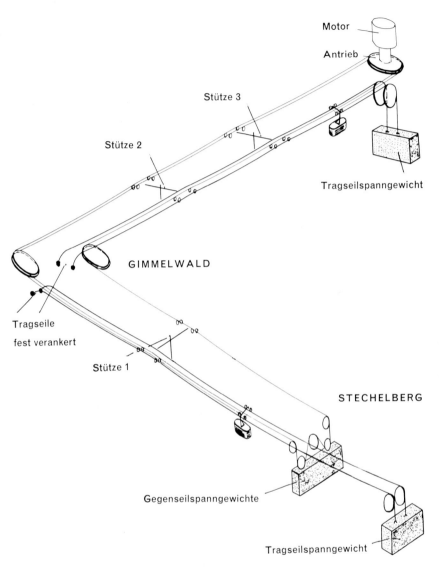

MÜRREN

Motor

Antrieb

Stütze 3

Stütze 2

Tragseilspanngewicht

GIMMELWALD

Tragseile
fest verankert

Stütze 1

STECHELBERG

Gegenseilspanngewichte

Tragseilspanngewicht

Sections 1 and 2 of the Schilthorn Cableway are linked, with Gimmelwald Station sitting exactly halfway timewise (another diagram on p. 28). One cabin goes to Mürren and one to Stechelberg. In a never-ending polonaise, the two cabins glide towards each other and then return to their stations. The passengers change cabins.

▶▶ *It is 27 km from the Schilthorn to the Wildstrubel. The telelens reaches out to fetch its stubborn peak, together with the nearby Hundshorn. Kandersteg lies in the deep valley between the two. To the right, the Wildhorn (white) and the Lohner (black).*

A song of thanksgiving is sung on the platform of the way station of Gimmelwald – the Schilthorn Cableway has linked the village with the great wide world.

The mobile attachment of the other end of the carrier cables is to ensure constantly equalized tension. To achieve this, the ends of the coupled, more flexible tensioning cables are led over deflection sheaves in a shaft and on them is hung a weight which moves freely on vertical rails. The travel of this tensioning carriage reflects, among other things, the moving load of the cabin and the greatest span between two cable supports. On the Birg, a 21 m shaft of Bond-like precision had to be made in the native rock. The dimensions of the counterweight shaft for the third section with its unusually bold span nearly 2 km in length exceeded even those on the Birg; this one had to be 25 m deep and 4.5 x 10 m in section, and all that despite Mürren's precarious moraine. The shaft was concreted in sections from the top downwards, one ring locking into place below the other. Today, on each of the two carrier cables of one track, a 31-ton concrete block dangles in this oubliette, and across both blocks lies a girder weighing another 12 tons. Thus, a carrier cable – which has an effective breaking load of 165 tons – is weighted to the tune of 36 tons, and in the highly unlikely event of one of the cable's ever snapping, the other would still be under a tension of 42 tons.

Manoeuvres in Gimmelwald

In April 1961 when the *foehn* was blowing full blast through the Wetter-lücke, coaxing the green buds out despite the old snow, the Mürren postman brought Ernst Feuz and Walter Amstutz the long-awaited news (for the attention of the Schilthorn Committee) that their application for permission to build an aerial cableway in four sections from Stechelberg via Gimmelwald, Mürren and Birg to the Schilthorn peak had been approved. The document went on to list the conditions that would be required. The authorities wanted heated lounges at the stations for both passengers and staff (this preoccupation with the welfare of the staff always goes hand in hand with a similar care for that of the passengers); they wanted barriers at danger points, signposts for skiers and wanderers; then there were building measures to be taken where the cableway crossed the high-tension cables of the Lauterbrunnen electricity works and in cases of col-

Number of passengers carried by the Schilthorn Cableway

Year	1st Section	2nd Section	3rd Section	4th Section	Average
1965	39 079	32 679	29 804	–	25 390
1966	123 190	111 163	91 973	–	81 581
1967	174 437	172 460	173 005	93 796	153 425
1968	182 146	184 997	150 440	138 578	164 040
1969	275 047	276 077	230 609	202 991	246 181
1970	295 137	299 873	250 324	231 743	269 269
1971	371 260	377 898	353 442	327 968	357 642
1972	303 601	330 598	302 139	275 450	302 947
1973	391 795	398 805	354 855	338 540	370 999
1974	405 374	414 002	370 979	354 252	386 152
1975	424 133	428 651	366 557	355 045	393 597
1976	425 381	433 014	382 712	376 008	404 279

lision with telephone cables. The ropeway had to be identified as a hindrance to flying. They required a "sufficiently large car-park to be laid out in Stechelberg"; a tunnel to open up the Saustal (later abandoned); and a weather-, snow- and avalanche-observation service whose duty it would be to decree an interruption in operation and keep the passengers informed should the necessity arise. The cableway was to operate all the year round between Stechelberg and Mürren, the timetable being adapted to the requirements of the little village of Gimmelwald, and the inhabitants of the municipality of Lauterbrunnen (which stretches from Wengen to Mürren) and those coming from farther afield to tend the alps and forests in the

The heart of the cableway is the winding gear where the headwheel is linked to the motor. The picture, taken at Mürren Station, shows the motor on the far right in front of two cable-driving sheaves. The constantly excited motor is fed with variable D.C. voltage by a superposed converter unit. To the left, in front of the gigantic counter-wheels, is the little winch for the auxiliary ropeway; for every self-respecting cableway has what human beings lack – a standby motor in case of a coronary. The emergency petrol motor (centre) can drive either the main shaft or the auxiliary ropeway.

Sefinen Valley were to benefit from reduced fares; the fares were not to undercut those on the existing Mürren Railway and, quite generally, there was to be co-operation both on the tariffs and the operating front with the Mürren, the Bernese Oberland and the Allmendhubel Railways, and the instructions of the supervisory authorities were to be strictly observed. From the diameter of the yellow navigation warning balls right down to its official name, "Luftseilbahn Stechelberg–Mürren–Schilthorn" or "LSMS" for short or "Schilthornbahn", the cradle of the new arrival was beribboned with official directives. And to ensure that it should never go hungry, even if Confederation and Canton should refuse any form of godparentage, special financial arrangements were made: after completion of the detailed planning, a new costs estimate was to be submitted together with a financial statement to the effect that a good 75–80% of the capital was company

The winding gear at Birg Station for the 4th section – equipped with only one traction cable as the gradient never exceeds 1 : 3.8 – has only one driving sheave and one counter-wheel. To make the arc of wrap larger, the traction cable is wound round an idling counter-wheel and despatched once more over the driving sheave – hence the two grooves in the wheels. To reduce the rotational speed, a two-stage gear is connected (gear casing shown). Left, the cast weights and magnets of the running and safety brake acting on the motor shaft.

stock and that outside capital amounted to at most 20–25% of the newly calculated building expenditure.

If the petitioners and initiators were in agreement with these various considerations, the Federal Department of Transport and Communications went on, they were to say so. The petitioners had in any case already offered free passes on the cableway to the vet, the doctor, the parson and the midwife in their original application. Let building commence, they replied optimistically – the capital would doubtless turn up in due time! The sky curved clear and blue over Mürren in October 1961 when the final documents arrived, bearing the signature of Federal Councillor Willy Spühler, Minister for Transport and Communications. With it came a yet further extended catalogue of federal wants – deadlines for the submitting of the financial statement, plans and models; more deadlines for the commence-

A cable head is about to be cast. The strands must be untwisted, the ends doubled over and spread out broom-fashion. The casting mould is then positioned. The cable head is made conical and rotates in a bushing hung on the running gear.

▼ The transverse sections of the carrier and traction cables used between Mürren and Birg. The carrier cable is of locked coil design with a mantle of 21 profile wires. A fine film of grease makes it completely watertight. The cable is 2980 m long and weighs 26015 kg. The traction cables are more pliable and weigh less: the lower traction cable weighs 8265 kg, the upper one, 9230 kg. Being Seale-type cables, each has six strands coiled around a hemp core, every strand consisting of a central wire with other wires wound around it in two layers of varying thickness.

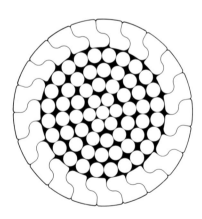

Carrier cable 40 mm
Completely locked coil construction
Outer wire coil 330 mm

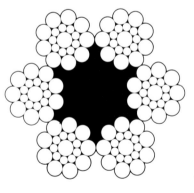

Lower traction cable 28.5 mm
Upper traction cable 30 mm
Stranded cable with Lang's lay to the right
Stranded coil 177 mm and 190 mm respectively

▼ *The 24-roller running van of a cabin in the 3rd section. Like the running van of all the cabins on the Schilthorn Cableway, this consists of a box-shaped main support with one beam facing up the mountain and the other facing down. There are four drop brakes in the beams (transverse boxes). Should one of the traction cables on the mountain side snap or slacken, the four pairs of bronze-lined brake jaws clamp themselves quick as lightning on to the carrier cable (in the supports they grab the cable shoe as well). If one of the traction cables on the valley side snaps or when the brake is manually activated from the cabin, the two pairs of brakes on the valley side only operate. Simultaneously the drive is switched off. The braking force is stored in strong springs and transmitted by a lever system. Vibration absorbers and torque rods in the suspension gear ensure gentle and balanced passage through the supports, when braking and in gusty winds. The telephone and signalling connections are made by the traction cable. Each cabin has a radio telephone.*

The large number of rollers permits a broad distribution of the cabin load on the carrier cables, for the bending stress as well as the surface pressure make tremendous demands on the life of the cable. This is why a soft, synthetic material is used to line the rollers. While also reducing noise, this hugs the cable closely, thus minimizing fulling and bending.

It took many years of experiment to find a lining of suitable quality and even now the rollers have to be constantly changed and relined. The same care is lavished on the bearings in the masts where the carrier cables are subjected to pressure both from above and below when the cabin crosses. The cable shoe is made wide and gently curved so that an abrupt bending of the cable is avoided. The location of the masts is also chosen with a view to reducing to a minimum the difference in declivity of a given stretch before and after each mast. The traction cable shoes on the masts in the Schilthorn Cableway have a 35 and 40 m radius of curvature. This also ensures smooth running of the cabins. Moreover, according to a Von Roll principle, all the cable counterweights have oil dampers which parry the strong, vertical vibrations in any rapid change of track gradient.

ment and completion of the work (which dates were to be at most 84 months apart); construction requirements concerning the adaptation to the surroundings of the architecture of the buildings (the technical supervisory authorities were, however, deaf and blind to the charms of shingle rooves); there were to be operating-noise abatement measures and a clause stipulating that the cableway be operated exclusively by trained personnel. It was a masterpiece of magisterial farsightedness – cableways were not just set up two-a-penny in Switzerland! (Licence for the Schilthorn Cableway granted the Schilthorn Committee on 23rd October 1961, valid for 20 years).

Considerations concerning the justification of a Schilthorn cableway brought the simultaneous refusal of an application submitted by others at the same time for permission to erect an aerial ropeway from the upper terminus of the Allmendhubel Railway to the level of the Schilthorn Hut at the mouth of the Engital. The ropeway was to be 960 m long over a total ascent of 525 m, with four supports and an intermediate stopping place as a makeshift, a carrier cable, an upper and a lower traction cable and two cabins for 20 or 30 passengers. The initiators reckoned with construction costs of something under Fr. 1.2 million and stated that a continuation of the ropeway up to the Schilthorn was not excluded (application submitted by the initiatory committee for a licence to build the Engital cableway, 13th July and 22nd September 1959). The advocates of the four-section Schilthorn cableway had armed themselves with Fr. 8.5 million; in the end the financial load grew to 30 million and demanded three increases in capital (application for a licence to build the Schilthorn cableway submitted by the Schilthorn Committee, 3rd, 5th and 22nd October, 5th November, 10th December 1959). If a soft, woolly lamb and a versicoloured giraffe had got together in the same preserve, their contrast would have been as nothing compared with that presented by the two ropeway projects in 1959, both of which wanted to achieve the same objective via a different route: the urgently necessary opening up of Mürren's ski and tourist hinterland. While the lamb grazed patiently on its conventional patch, the Engital cableway being merely considered as a prolongation of the existing railways, the giraffe stretched out both above and below. The ranginess of the giraffe was reflected in the line chosen for the Schilthorn cableway which reached directly to the main road precisely where there was still room for a carpark in the valley, and then angled off to connect the village of Gimmelwald – thus far accessible only on foot – with the main lines of communication. It then continued up to the Schilthorn to deal Mürren and the valley a touristic trump. (See p. 28).

Behind the spectacular profile of this ambitious animal was Ernst Feuz, the leading initiator of the project, who understood the predicament of the little alpine farmer and knew every last cranny in Lauterbrunnental. The

Mürren's weatherman lives in the Wetterlücke between the Breithorn and the Tschingel-horn. He goes, above all, by the sun, wind and clouds in the Rhône Valley which shine on or shadow the mountain terrace at Mürren, taking little heed of the forecast for the northern part of the country.

son of a mountain guide, he grew up in Mürren as one of a large family and then set out into the business world. As a far-sighted career man in a depart-ment store concern, Ernst Feuz knew all about the tingling delights of start-ing something new, of large-scale calculation, organizing, seeking and finding. He took charge of the technical planning which was already ripe for negotiations in the summer of 1959; he looked after the licensing, the financing, the building terrain, the overcrossing rights, the expertise of ava-lanche specialists – and he had the local inhabitants behind him. The Mayor of Lauterbrunnen was forced to transfer the extraordinary council meeting – convened at the request of two hundred voters – from the schoolhouse to the church. At that time, on 9th April 1960, the question under discussion was the future of Stechelberg, Gimmelwald and Mürren. Along the nave and up in the galleries, a great majority of the citizens raised their hands, their demand for the Schilthorn cableway ringing out across the canton to the Houses of Parliament in Berne. The application for a concession was accompanied by 300 signatures.

Sports and Games

When the stately "Wega" was inflated in the Place d'Armes at Sion in October 1898 and lifted off for the first triumphant flight over the Alps, carrying 1600 kg of ballast, the balloonist Edouard Spelterini, the geologist Albert Heim, a meteorologist and one paying passenger, 115 years had passed since a "Charlière" had been set upon with flails, pitch-forks and other agricultural implements in the village of Gonesse near Paris. In order to put paid to that cosmic apparition, the farmers punctured and slashed it, finishing up by harnessing a horse to its comet's tail and dragging it across the fields. That was the inglorious end of the first hydrogen balloon.

Before this new star could be launched, however, a vast amount of money and ingenuity had been expended. First of all, a gas-producing device had to be invented. After lengthy deliberation the physicist, Jacques A.C. Charles – hence "Charlière" – decided to put iron filings and water into a barrel with two holes in the upper end. In one of the holes was a leather tube leading to the balloon and through the other they dribbled sulphuric acid. The heat generated was soon so tremendous that acid-laden steam also flowed into the envelope where it threatened to eat holes in the silk fabric and had to be constantly sprayed to keep it cool. To fill the balloon it needed several days of hard work and anxious waiting, 1000 lbs of iron and 500 lbs of sulphuric acid. The experiment showed that the difficulties could be overcome by channelling the gas through a large vessel of water to eliminate the acid vapours. At the end of the fourth day the balloon, two-thirds inflated, was lashed to a yoke and borne with the gas machine to the Champs de Mars near the Military Academy, at dead of night, accompanied by torchbearers and the patrolling guard. Anyone meeting this extraordinary procession was inclined to doubt the evidence of his own eyes. But when the fully inflated balloon took to the clouds the following afternoon, it was seen off with a salute of guns and the unrestrained jubilation of 200,000 people.

Among the spectators was Stephan Montgolfier who, in his turn, was busy designing an even better air balloon. The brothers, Stephan and Joseph Montgolfier, succeeded for the first time in June 1783 in constructing a balloon for a load of 400 lbs. Contrary to the later "Charlière", this one was filled with hot air. Until they learned that the force driving their airship was

A free balloon being inflated at Mürren. In the competition for the Grand Prize of the Schilthorn Cableway it is – for once – not the speed from point to point that counts; nor are duration, altitude and distance assessed, but simply the all-round performance: safety, navigation of the balloon and accurate logging which must allow of scientific exploitation.

The world is spread out at the feet of the Schilthorn. It is up to the visitors to exploit to the full the freedom offered. This will take them up hill and down dale, over meadows and white-mantled fields.
The Niesen and the Lake of Thoune; above the fog-blanketed plain lies the Jura.

merely heat-thinned air, the brothers believed that, by burning a mixture of damp straw and picked wool, an electric vapour must be formed which would force the balloon into the skies. A new Montgolfière launched in Versailles in the presence of the King and another goodly crowd carried a sheep, a rooster and a duckling. And on 21st November 1783 the first manned balloon flight took place. Pilâtre de Rozier and the Marquis d'Arlande were seated in a gallery beneath the billowing silk of an even more magnificent Montgolfière, with the glowing fire beside them so that they could constantly maintain the flame. According as the voyagers fed the fire, the airship rose or sank. A few days later, Paris was treated to yet another balloon spectacle – Charles and his assistant, Robert, had prepared a balloon filled with washed hydrogen which already had all the equipment of the perfected Charlière, including the butterfly valve in the upper curve, by opening which the balloon could be brought down at will. The flight lasted nine hours.

Nowhere is hiking more exhilarating than where the winds swirl and eddy. A new, safe-guarded mountain footpath leads from the Schilthorn down to the Saustal (see map on pp. 116/117).
The Lobhörner as seen through the windows of the restaurant at the peak.

"It is a newborn babe," replied Benjamin Franklin, who happened to be in Paris, when asked about the possible uses of the free balloon. The new arrival was hindered in that it was – and still is – steerable only to a limited degree; for it was only by reaching altitudes where the air current moved in the required direction that the pilot was enabled to head for a given objective. With the experience of about 500 display flights behind him, Spelterini was to fly the "Wega" from Sion into the Rhine Valley in the region of St. Gallen, but instead of going eastwards, the wind carried it almost straight over the glaciers of the Diablerets and into France. In August 1910 Spelterini – whose real name was Edouard Schweizer – was preparing in Mürren for a new adventure: a flight to the south over the high mountains. His "Sirius", a gas balloon like the "Wega" but only half the size with its 1500 cubic metres of volume, carried him in brilliant sunshine over the Matterhorn and into the foothills near Turin! In 1957, when specialized aeronautical knowledge about those early alpine flights had dwindled to the

literary reports of the pioneers, the pilot, Fred Dolder, gave a repeat performance of that epic pioneer undertaking. He was supported by the Swiss Foundation for Alpine Research and two Everest climbers. Since then Mürren has been the Mecca of balloonists and the scene of the annual International High Alpine Dolder Ballooning Weeks. There could be no more ideal starting place than this village – an alpine balcony in a wind-sheltered hollow against a mountain backdrop of breathtaking beauty.

Was it really necessary for the "newborn babe" to earn its salt? Even now, two hundred years later, the wicker-basket of the gentle globe in royal purple still maintains its superiority over all other vehicles: floating among the clouds and yet so near the earth, soundless, open, in harmony with the deep quiet, the winds and the vast expanse of the heavens, it is the very essence of mankind's eternal dream.

Another favourite pastime in Mürren is skiing – that godlike cavorting and gliding among the beauties Nature has so lavishly spread around. In the deep snow and *sulz* on the slopes of the Schilthorn, highspirited youngsters laid the foundations of the Swiss University Ski Club, the Kandahar Ski Club, the British Ladies' Ski Club and the Swiss Ladies' Ski Club. In Mürren in 1931 the first World Championships took place in the alpine disciplines created there – downhill and slalom.

In all this *perpetuum mobile,* the cabins of the Schilthorn cableway today collaborate manfully with the tireless skiers. The unquenchable thirst for speed of the relentless downhill racers forces the red gondolas to keep up a brisk pace. And so they go on their uninterrupted way – up, down, up, down… From November to May they are stormed by hordes of skiers of all

◄◄ *The Schilthorn enthroned over glittering ski slopes. The prepared piste reaches out in a wide curve through the Engital, follows the course of the Ägertenbach (extreme right) and hops across the Allmendhubel (lower left) into the Blumental – a 6 km run descending 1300 m.*

◄ *It was the Englishman, Arnold Lunn, who created the modern slalom in Mürren – that slicing, twisting, plunging and swerving between pairs of flags –, another of those games that help make life worth living. Mürren was well on the way to becoming a winter sports resort.*

87

Schiltalp	1 Std. 10 Min.		Blumental	40 Min.	
Grauseeli	2 Std. 50 Min.	Mürren	Allmendhubel	1 Std.	
Schilthorn	4 Std. 40 Min.	1640 m	Schilthornhütte	2 Std. 50 Min.	
Station Birg	3 Std. 20 Min.		Schilthorn	4 Std. 40 Min.	
Gimmeln	45 Min.		Grütschalp	1 Std. 25 Min.	
Boganggen	2 Std.		Isenfluh	2 Std. 30 Min.	
Sefinenfurgge	4 Std.		Saustal	2 Std. 30 Min.	
Griesalp / Kiental	6 Std.		Lauterbrunnen	1 Std. 30 Min.	
			Gimmelwald	45 Min.	
			Stechelberg	1 Std. 45 Min.	
			Sefinental	1 Std.	
			Obersteinberg	4 Std. 10 Min.	

Where do all the footpaths lead? The signpost at Mürren Station answers your question. The arrows on a white ground indicate mountain footpaths.

classes. The veterans start the gallop down the mountainside precisely at the peak, whose slopes are as exhilarating as bubbling champagne. Although the uppermost part of the run is quite steep, it tapers off in the traverse of the Seelifuhre where the bubbles of the initial intoxication start to settle. People who prefer a milder version choose Birg, behind whose forbidding rock fortress lie the gentle slopes of the Engital where snow is assured until well into the spring. One crosses the hollow with wings on one's skis and each descent is a kind of unchained delight. A ski-lift tows the skiers willingly from the floor of the valley back to Birg station. Those who like it really hot

◄◄ *A walking tour need not start at the peak – here, the starting-point was Birg Station or Mürren or Gimmelwald. The paths around Mürren offer less ambitious walks tailored to suit an average pair of legs. – View from the country lane leading from Mürren into the Schilttal. Just behind the cabin on the 2nd section of the Schilthorn Cableway is the mast of its transport ropeway. In the background, the Lauberhorn and the Grindelwald Wetterhorn over the saddle of the Kleine Scheidegg; to the right, the Eiger and the Schwarzmönch casting its shadow over the Trümmletental.*

Boots with profiled soles are an advisable precaution for crossing the ridge of the Schilt-horn to the Rote Herd.

will take the fast run via the Schilthorn Hut, leaping, gliding and swaying, passing the narrow Kanonenrohr in wide sweeps and making for the All-mendhubel without pause. Here, a snap decision must be made – to the left of the knobbly mountain nose the skier enters the attractive ski carrousel of Winteregg where the midwinter madness gently subsides among the delights of this wooded hill country; to the left also lies the route of the legendary Inferno Race which has already been run about thirty times; it covers a difference in altitude of 2000 m with a tricky, horizontal stretch, and is the longest and most entertaining downhill race in the world. Anyone can attempt it who, with 1200 other competitors, feels up to running the gauntlet of this daredevil challenge from the Schilthorn down to Lauter-brunnen. – To the right of the Allmendhubel, in the bowl of the Blumental, the red gondolas and the other ski-lifts invite the skier to another downhill run. The 500 m ride up to the starting-point of the classical Kandahar racing run in the lee of the Schiltgrat must not be overlooked. Here, too, the sweet-toothed can cross the sun-drenched alps of the Schilt in broad sweeps, skiing into the Wintertal and then back to Mürren by way of dessert. And why not?

The kirsch in the coffee is the fast run to Gimmelwald which leads directly to the station and the red gondolas.

The menu given here does not mean that the touring skier is at a disadvantage either in the matter of downhill runs or in the planning of his day. One of the most attractive objectives in the Schilthorn region is the quiet wonder of the Saustal over which the Schwalmere presides. The tour starts at the peak with an 800 m walk along the ridge – safeguarded by ropes and steps – and then drops to the northern slope of the Rote Herde. Hundshorn, Sefinenalp and the Kiental are other magic formulae.

A well-earned rest on the Suppenalp in the Blumental. Mast 5 on the Schiltgrat gazes hungrily into the plates.

Dry Run – the Funicular Railway

In the portrait gallery of the funicular railways – themselves quite respectable – the same pictures are to be found on many of the walls as appear in the gallery of the modern aerial cableway: that is to say, the inevitable portraits of mining railways. The unmistakable features of a common forebear are particularly striking both in the to-and-fro system for the aerial cableway and in the funicular – the arrangement of the self-acting inclined plane, that exemplary invention of a penny-conscious time when people

Main specifications and capacities of the Mürren and Allmendhubel Railways

	Allmendhubel Funicular Railway	Lauterbrunnen– Grütschalp Funicular Railway	Grütschalp– Mürren Adhesion Railway
Year of opening	1912	1891	1891
Length of line	536 m	1421 m	4274 m
Lower terminus (metres above sea-level)	1649	796	1487
Upper terminus (metres above sea-level)	1907	1481	1638
Total ascent	258 m	685 m	151 m
Maximum gradient	1 : 1.6	1 : 1.6	1 : 20
Rolling stock	2 passenger coaches with seating for 65 persons	2 passenger coaches with seating for 62 persons	4 motorcoaches for a total of 360 pers.
		2 goods wagons	4 open goods wagons 2 maintenance cars
Speed	3.3 m/s	2.5 m/s	
Hourly passenger capacity in one direction	580	328	
Passengers carried:			
1965	132 673		376 271
1970	188 821		449 029
1975	242 442		576 078

knew how to turn the force of gravity into a perfected means of conveyance, using a rope, a slanting groove and a roller to reduce the friction. To make the cabin coming down haul the other one up the hill, all that is needed is a "topping-up" output to compensate the difference in weight and the motion loss. The driving force can be helped along – or even replaced – by a winch. After the invention of the steam engine, the manual winch was replaced by a steam winch and later on came the electric motor.

When it was opened in August 1891 the cable railway of the two-section Mürren Railway had no winch at Grütschalp Station, but merely a horizontal deflecting pulley for the traction cable connecting the two coaches. The impetus required to set the downward coach in motion was given by overweight in the form of water ballast. The increasing weight of the cable on the downward journey was carefully compensated by a gradual emptying of the water tank by the conductor. It could nevertheless occur that, in the concave section just before the lower terminus, the passengers had to be despatched among the rubble to forage for fresh ballast for the railcar!

The robust wall which carried the railway had a sandwich layer of longitudinal larchwood sleepers strongly anchored with bolts and bedded in reinforced concrete. The permanent way was clamped to this foundation, with three stretches of rail for two, one-metre-gauge tracks – except at the crossing where four running rails were laid. Each track had a ladder rack at one side for the brake pinions and a paved gutter for the ballast water to flow into. In addition, there was a continuous flight of steps along the centre of the crest and lateral catwalks with balustrades on the viaducts. To prevent the coaches lifting off the rails, claws were attached to their undersides to grip the upper flanges of the rack. And, as in all steep railways, the coaches were fitted with spindle brakes and automatic drop brakes (operatable both from the upper and the lower platform and acting on the brake drums of both gearwheel axles), as well as with a mechanical governor that triggered the automatic brakes as soon as the permissible speed was exceeded.

▶▶ *The old funicular benefitted in its turn from the technical perfecting of its cousin, the aerial cableway. Both have cable traction, a fixed drive with winding gear, usually two cabins which arrive and depart simultaneously, have the same travelling speed and cross midway. The Lauterbrunnen–Grütschalp funicular opened in 1891 on a 1 : 1.6 gradient track. The water ballast was carried in the undercarriage.*

▶ *Cable-bearing rollers.*

The engineers always aim to give a funicular the ideal longitudinal profile of a parabola or cycloid, i.e. the shape of a hammock, which ensures constant tractive power. However, the longer the railway, the more difficult it becomes to maintain the theoretical profile, and the greater the deviations, the more water has to be carried; and the more massive the construction of the coach body and the cable, the fewer the passengers the train can carry. There was room for forty in the open panorama coach on the Mürren Railway, and when it got chilly they simply wrapped themselves up in blankets and drew the curtains. The journey lasted 25 minutes – far too long, lamented the crowd at the terminus that had to wait for the next train because of shortage of space.

At that time electricity as a tractive force was being introduced only very hesitatingly, but mature consideration would have allowed its use from the start instead of nearly ten years later – the adhesion railway in the second section was planned to be electrically driven – and it was only consideration for a nervous public which prevented the use of electricity for the cable railway. For the 1902 season an electric driving disk with dual transmission and the cable wound three times around the driving pulley was installed at the upper terminus; the railway's own turbine house on the Staubbach was strengthened by means of a powerful storage battery; a new stranded wire cable was ordered, only 34 mm in diameter but affording eightfold safety;

Who was the gifted draughtsman? None other than the relievo artist, Xaver Imfeld, drew up the application for a concession to build a two-section, narrow-gauge railway from Lauterbrunnen to Mürren. It was dated 28th February and received a hearing during the same year. For on 29th April 1887 Parliament approved the construction of a narrow-gauge railway from Interlaken to Lauterbrunnen. The first section of the Mürren Railway is run as a funicular, the second as an adhesion railway.

and two bigger coaches were purchased, each with seating for 60 people. It was now the engineer on the platform in the upper terminus who regulated the progress of the train by means of the prescribed braking installations.

A few years later, the parabola was given a longer leg when the railway dam was extended to the station shared by the Bernese Oberland Railways and the Wengernalp Railway. No wonder that those responsible for the Mürren railway turned a deaf ear to the simultaneous demand of the Mürren hoteliers for a winter timetable!

But what happened to the old rails with the toothed racks? Between 1948 and 1950 the railway underwent a full-scale overhaul, during which all the old accessories disappeared and the journey time was reduced to 11 minutes. The permanent way was simplified and reduced to two strong rails, a new cable was laid, light metal coaches were bought and a new building housing a rapid drive was erected at the upper terminus. Toothed rack, braking pinion and the third rail were thrown overboard, and the coaches now have emergency drop brakes with pincer-like brake shoes – just like the gondolas on the aerial cableway. What is more, the silver coaches of the Mürren Railway at the Lauterbrunnen gateway are suspended on their cable by a cast head in a bushing precisely like the red gondolas of the Schilthorn cableway at the backdoor in Stechelberg. So there you are! The difference in altitude is the same back and front, but between them lies the romance of a village that has retained its rugged originality – a village blessedly free from roads and traffic noise.

Top: world première on the mountain terrace in Mürren! In 1891 the rolling stock of the 2nd section of the Lauterbrunnen–Mürren Railway consisted of two goods wagons, two passenger coaches and – wonder of wonders – 3 locomotive engines! (That same year – while there was still no electrically-driven engine on any main-line railway – the first electric tramway went into operation in Halle). Engine BLM No. 3 had two axles, each with its own 4-pole, 25 horsepower motor with serial winding. The driving axles were driven via a spur gear. The body of the passenger coach rested on two bogies. It naturally held as many passengers as the cableway cabin. In addition to two closed compartments, it had an open central section with 26 folding seats where the passengers could enjoy the sun and the view. The railway operated only in summer.

Below: with the help of fast motorcoaches, the timetable on the Lauterbrunnen–Mürren stretch offers 40 pairs of trains a day; the journey – including the change – takes 30 minutes. In conjunction with a trip up the Schilthorn (circular-tour tickets are available), the film of indelible impressions takes on new dimensions. The Mönch and his radiant Jungfrau are largely responsible for this (Jungfraujoch between the two).

The Valley of the Waterfalls

Should you happen to meet the good fairy of Gimmelwald, the best thing to wish for is a sunny day-off round about the time of the May thaw! For it is a sight not to be missed when the spring *foehn* melts the snowfields and the névé and the valley walls around Lauterbrunnen overflow like a full pot under the water-tap! Just as the fields bejewel themselves at blossom time, so too do the cliffs hang out their pennants and streamers. The waters erupt over the clifftops like flags in the wind, cascade into the void, disintegrate into clouds of spume and join up again, rushing and gurgling, in the silvery streamlet at the mountain foot. The Weisse Lütschine collects anything that

The first funicular railways in Switzerland

Funicular	Year of opening	Length of line in m	Maxi- mum gradient	Gauge in cm	Rack system	Original traction
Lausanne–Ouchy	1877	2456	1 : 8	143.5	–	Water turbine
Giessbach	1879	331	1 : 3	100	R	Water balance
Territet–Glion	1883	560	1 : 1.7	100	R	Water balance
Gütsch (Lucerne)	1884	159	1 : 1.9	100	R	Water balance
Marzili (Berne)	1885	105	1 : 3	75	R	Water balance
Lugano–Stazione	1886	243	1 : 4	100	A	Water balance
Biel–Magglingen	1887	1633	1 : 3	100	R	Water balance
Bürgenstock	1888	831	1 : 1.7	100	A	Electric motor
Zürichberg	1889	171	1 : 3.8	100	A	Electric motor
Beatenberg	1889	1610	1 : 2.5	100	R	Water balance
Salvatore, 2 sections	1890	1524	1 : 1.6	100	A	Electric motor
Ecluse–Plan	1890	379	1 : 2.6	100	R	Water balance
Lauterbrunnen– Grütschalp	1891	1212	1 : 1.6	100	R	Water balance

In the case of water-balance operation, the racks were necessary for the coach brakes and were generally removed after electrification. On the other hand, the Lausanne–Ouchy funicular was turned into a rack-and-pinion railway in 1958.
The Lauterbrunnen–Grütschalp funicular was already electrified in 1902 and, like nearly all the funiculars listed here, was simultaneously slightly lengthened.

is going, wellsprings or glacier streams, and leads them – tumbling joyfully in their sunlit bed – through verdant river-meadows and flower-studded fields on their way out of the valley. But this idyllic picture changes abruptly at the rapids under the Steinschlagwald where the waters go mad again, the waves rearing up and cavorting to their own thunderous music, smacking

In 1830 frock coats, tight-laced bodices and poke bonnets did not prevent people from tackling the onerous path to Lauterbrunnen to admire the Staubbach so extolled by poets and artists. Mine host at the Steinbock Hotel (already three storeys high) kept a very respectable table and had coaches and well-saddled mountain horses ready for his guests as well. (The veduta is unsigned).

down on driftwood and round-headed stones – and still more water keeps flowing down! In Zweilütschinen, the clear, white Lauterbrunnen Lütschine meets the Grindelwald Lütschine, blackened by the slate drift on the Faulhorn chain, and together they flow into the Lake of Brienz.

Four reasons are mooted for the awakening from the dull indifference of the Middle Ages to a feeling for the beauty of primitive alpine Nature: a physical need to regenerate spiritual resources in the clear mountain air; the advances made by the exact sciences in the mapping, measuring and researching of glaciers and alpine wildernesses; the sense of achievement in negotiating great heights (in conjunction with the craving to scan far horizons); and the formation of a romantic and vital consciousness. Because everything in the two Lütschinen valleys conspired to achieve such perfection, the whole region has been the objective – ever since this awakening to the beauties of the Alps – of a never-ending stream of tourists

The seignorial vicarage in Lauterbrunnen, built in 1780 in the style of a manor house, was intended by the State to serve also to accommodate travellers. In those days, playing host was the vicar's secondary rôle. A year earlier Goethe stayed at the homey old presbytery with Mr. Unger, the vicar.

which has kept increasing more or less in step with the changes in Europe's political times. Forty years before the first modest hotel, the Silberhorn in Mürren was built, the author of that thorough handbook, *Reise in das Berner Oberland* (Journey to the Bernese Oberland), decided to boycott all the old engravings and either entirely to ban from his illustrations all "well-known objects such as the Staubbach and the Jungfrau" or to depict them from an unusual angle. This attitude was entirely justified, for at that time – 1816 – artists like Aberli, Wolf, Dunker, Lory, König, Rieter, Lafond, Birmann and Meyer had already taken good care that such objects, set in decorative and idyllic veduta, were suitably propagated among the travelling public, spurred on as they were to the production of models for engravings and aquatints by publishers and printers with an eye to the best chance. However, this did not stop Mr. Wyss devoting 20 pages of his guide to a description of the "hundredfold described, painted and engraved" Staubbach, its configuration and its might on fair days and foul, in summer, in high winds and in winter, and advising the reader under no circumstances to miss the hour-long walk to the upper Staubbach Fall, being sure to reach the station before 9 or 10 a.m.

The itinerary for romantic cultural tours had also progressed by leaps and bounds. It led almost exclusively from Berne via Thoune and the Lake of

The main peaks immediately surrounding the Schilthorn and their ascent

Peak	Metres above Sea-level	First Climbed	Customary Route*
Jungrau	4158	1811	From Jungfraujoch or Concordia Huts via Rottalsattel and the south-eastern ridge – easy
Wetterhorn	3701	1844	From Gleckstein Hut via the Krinnen Glacier and the Wettersattel – middling
Mönch	4099	1857	From Jungfraujoch or the Bergli Hut via the south-east arm of the eastern ridge – easy to middling
Eiger	3970	1858	From Eigergletscher via the south-west flank and the western ridge – middling
Blümlisalphorn	3664	1860	From Blümlisalp Hut via the north-west ridge – middling
Breithorn	3782	1865	From Mutthorn Hut via the Wetterlücke and the west ridge – middling
Tschingelhorn	3577	1865	From Mutthorn Hut via the south side – easy
Gletscherhorn	3983	1867	From Hollandia or Concordia Huts via Gletscherjoch and the west ridge – middling
Ebnefluh	3960	1868	From Hollandia Hut via Ebnefluhfirn – easy
Grosshorn	3762	1868	Via Hintere Lücke and the south ridge – middling
Gspaltenhorn	3437	1869	From Gspaltenhorn Hut via Büttlassenlücke and the north-west ridge – middling
Mittaghorn	3897	1878	From Hollandia Hut via Anenjoch and the south-east ridge – easy

* "Easy" means that it is generally not necessary to use one's hands. It must, however, be borne in mind that unfavourable conditions, sudden changes in the weather, inadequate equipment and lack of physical training and experience can turn even the easiest mountain expedition into a difficult and hazardous undertaking. "Middling" means of a medium degree of difficulty.

▶▶ *The water roars and froths over the Mürren wall. During the thaw, in April and May, the cliffs in the Lauterbrunnen Valley run with water. The young foliage in the spring woods blazes softly green and myriads of gay flower-faces smile from the meadows. Why can't time stand still? – Grosshorn, Staubbach Fall.*

Thoune to Unterseen and thence into the valleys of Lauterbrunnen and Grindelwald – possibly taking in the Breithorn Glacier, and the two Scheideggs –, and back to Berne via Meiringen. It was *the* journey which afforded a maximum of tremendous scenic impressions, whereby the natural science curriculum was enriched by the viewing of natural rock sections (see p. 26!), glacier tongues and waterfalls. "As the many travellers who came to the region every year to visit the Alps and the glaciers always required brief instruction," Johann Samuel Wyttenbach published the itinerary in a small pocketbook in 1777, forty years before Mr. Wyss published his guide. The sights of particular interest were given special consideration and the Staubbach was praised as being one of the most magnificent, and if one wanted to view the glorious rainbow which formed in the lower basin, one was advised to choose a morning for the visit. Oh, those rainbows which so delight the eye when the sun at one's back shines on the swirling waterdrops! The

An innovation is announced – "Téléphon à Mürren." The private wire linked the Steinbock Hotel in Lauterbrunnen with the Hôtel des Alpes in Mürren. The two hotels acted as relay for an affiliated carrier enterprise whose 80 horses went just as well over the St. Gotthard Pass as they did on the Schilthorn.

The villages of Lauterbrunnen, Wengen, Stechelberg, Gimmelwald and Mürren have always formed a single political community, the "Talschaft Lauterbrunnen." A few years ago, little Isenfluh – slowly becoming depopulated – was also taken into the stronghold. Lauterbrunnen circa 1920, looking up the valley.

spectrum had already fascinated the universal spirit of Albrecht Haller in 1732 – shortly after publication of his narrative poem, *Die Alpen.* He wrote, "I have seen the rainbow and I stood for hours observing this rare phenomenon. It is completely elliptical, bends low over the tips of the grass, and has no sharp reds, but yellow, green and blue." Johann Wolfgang Goethe, pursuant to the advice obtained personally from Wyttenbach in Berne and taking a leaf out of Haller's book, dedicated his *Gesang der Geister über den Wassern* to the Staubbach in October 1779. In the literature of the *Sturm und Drang* period, the waterfall was regarded as the symbol of an optimistic overflowing of emotion and the elemental force of life. But Goethe also succumbed to the fascination of light refraction in a prisma or crystal-clear body and went so far as to draw up a theory of colour – although no one took this very seriously after Newton.

But why not go and see the waterfalls of Lauterbrunnen for yourself!

The Walsers at the Backdoor

The prosaic reverse of this new awareness of the mountains manifested itself in the developing aid answering the ruling principles of laissez-faire; a tourist industry was set up. Life in the remote mountain valleys was difficult enough in all conscience. And if the pixies had not frequented the steep upper slopes and cut the perfumed grass in the night so that the work was already half done when the haymakers arrived at dawn – in other words, if young and old had not laboured incessantly from daybreak till far into the night, the valley inhabitants would never have found a livelihood. For wherever slovenliness and idleness reigned, the helpful spirits vanished without warning, never to return. Gnomes, lost souls, snakes and the giants of heathen legend lurked with evil intent at the first sign of human weakness.

The thing about the hundred-hour working week was that a large part of it was spent getting to work. The mountain farm devoted to cattle-breeding and dairying extends over various altitudes. It consists in general of three parts: the winter quarters with dwelling house, tilled land and rich fattening pasture, the *Maiensässen* or *Vorsassen* which serve as pastureland in spring and autumn and sometimes provide hay in the summer, and the alpine pastures on the higher slopes where the herds graze in midsummer. The mountain farmer is constantly on the move seeking pasture for his cattle. Part of the time he wanders with his cows from stable to stable, from pasture to pasture, from the valley to the alp and down again, and for the rest of the time he follows his cattle around with stocks of hay. And only the very best herbs are allowed into the fodder – lady's mantle, milk-vetch and hawkweed, clover and alpine plantain, feverfew, spignel and meadow-grass. And woe betide anyone who allows dock and stinging nettle into the fodder! Thus, in addition to tillage, forest and meadows, the mountain farmer has to tend and cultivate the open pastureland and the alp, for if they are not properly looked after, they harden and become a stony wilderness; and if the pasturing on the slopes ceases, the grass lies down and becomes a slipway for avalanches. The process of earth erosion is also a factor not to be neglected.

The flat floor of the Lauterbrunnen Valley was settled late. The temperamental course of the untamed Lütschine River made the valley

Seventy waterfalls are said to flow into the Weisse Lütschine in the Lauterbrunnen Valley. "Lauter lautere Brunnen…" – "Limpid streams everywhere…" One of the most beautiful of the waterfalls is the Mürrenbach, alleged to be the highest in Europe. It is precisely here that the builder of the Schilthorn Cableway found the ledge which enabled him to halve the Mürren wall. The rock slopes down towards Gimmelwald.

The Lobhörner, 2566 m, directly above Isenfluh in the Lauterbrunnen Valley – a miniature paradise for climbers practising for greater things. The stony teeth are approached from the Lobhorn Hut picturesquely situated above the Sulssee at 1955 m.

trough uninhabitable and it was only on the higher slopes that protection against flood was ensured. The first settlements were in Wengen, in Gimmelwald and in Mürren. While the inhabitants of Wengen came from the Aare Valley, those who settled in the remote reaches of the upper Lauterbrunnen Valley – in Gimmelwald, Mürren and the hamlets of Sichellauenen and Trachsellauenen, as well as in Ammerten which has since disappeared – were emigrants from the Lötschen Valley in the south. These people came – some of them voluntarily, some of them under coercion – through a backdoor from the Valais. First mention of Lötschental emigrants in Lauterbrunnental was found in a document dated 1331, connecting them with the church at Gsteig. This document concerns interest on Sefinen alpine rights owed the monastery at Interlaken. A title deed dated 1346 bears witness to the long arm of the Augustinians and the existence of the Walsers in the Bernese Oberland. This time, however, the latter were the passive party to the deal. The freeman, Peter zum Turn of Gestelen, quite simply sold to the monastery in Interlaken "the people brought hither

In the Middle Ages there were mines in Stechelberg for iron, lead and zinc. During the interfolding of the crystalline earth strata with younger Triassic layers a number of ore deposits emerged from the molten interior to reach the surface of the earth in the upper valley. The furnace shown here stands on the right bank of the river just before Zweilütschinen and is about 340 years old. Here, the iron oolite mined in the Rottal above was smelted. Vast tracts of forest were carbonized in the process.

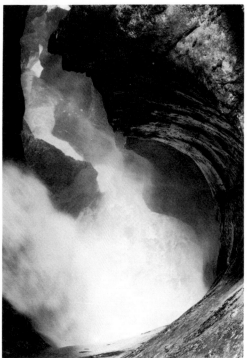

The Trümmelbach, gushing and roaring through round potholes in a narrow gorge, also tells of the might of the earth's forces appearing in Lauterbrunnen Valley. Unaided, it drains the vast ice clefts on the Eiger, Mönch and Jungfrau high overhead. To admire the spectacle of the seven glacier waterfalls, one rides on a single-cabin ropeway obliquely upwards inside the rock. The counterweight hanging on the cable flashes under the moving wagon in the illuminated shaft.

111

by himself and his forebears", for the sake of his own soul and that of his mother buried in the monastery gardens – plus 300 golden guilders. The marriage of the noble Peter's parents had united the all-powerful feudal families of Gestelen-Raron in the Valais and Wädiswil from the northern slopes of the Alps; their son and grandson preferred gold to the family property. From then on the Lötschental people had to pay their tithe of corn and their taxes to Interlaken.

Because the canons insisted on regular attendance at the church in Gsteig, the valley people took action and built a church of their own in 1487, imported a bell duly ordered from their old home – the yoke on which it was transported was discovered during rebuilding in 1830 – and had their church consecrated by the Bishop of Lausanne in person. In this way, Lauterbrunnen became the hub of the valley. A satisfactory *modus vivendi* with the monastery had just been found when the secularization pursued by

Gimmelwald, the Walser village in the sun-filled bowl between Stechelberg and Mürren. Each rooftop peeps into a carefully tended garden where peas and beans compete with lupins and gillyflowers. A good dollop of dung – and there's no shortage of cows – promotes healthy growth even at higher altitudes. The results make the townfolk green with envy.

the Bernese aristocracy gained a foothold in the course of the Reformation. The parishioners were prepared to accept the new doctrine only if they were exempted from payment of the interest and tithes on the confiscated monastery property. This led to revolt and, in 1528, to a murderous defeat and bloody vengeance. In gratitude for their help against the refractory farmers,

The first tourist aerial cableways on the to-and-fro system in Switzerland

Cableway	Year of opening	Length of line m	Total ascent m	Intermediate supports	Passengers in each of the two cabins	Speed m/s	Hourly passenger capacity in one direction
Wetterhorn, 1st s.*	1908	556	420	–	16	1	100
Gerschnialp–Trübsee, 1st section	1927	2227	531	6	33	6	210
Schwägalp–Säntis**	1935	2157	1121	3	35	4	175
Beckenried–Klewenalp**	1936	3108	1144	9	20	4	83
Champéry–Planachaux	1939	1660	705	2	18	4	120
Riddes–Isérables	1942	1988	617	3	12	4	160
Stöckalp–Melchsee**	1945	3435	823	13	8	4	32
Raron–Unterbäch	1950	2160	588	6	16	6	135
Klosters–Gotschnagrat, 1st s.	1950	2953	1097	7	40	6	280
** 2nd s.					24	5.5	300
Mörel–Greicheralp**	1951	2810	1143	11	12	6	50
Kandersteg–Stock	1951	1580	625	2	16	6	170

* The Wetterhorn cableway, of which only the 1st section was built, was closed in 1914 and dismantled in 1934. ** The technical installations were later altered to increase the capacity of the cableway.

Berne made the town of Unterseen a gift of the mountain rights on the Sefinen Alp! The best alpine pastureland was thus bartered to people outside the valley.

Stark privation haunted the eyes of the people in the forgotten valley when Johann Samuel Wyttenbach – he who wrote the little guide in 1777 – came from Berne to visit his fellow-priest near the Staubbach Fall. He wanted to know whether something could not be done for these poor people and suggested setting up a cottage industry. Visitors before Wyttenbach had made similar proposals and there had been experiments with crystal-cutting,

At the backdoor in Gimmelwald. The stony path plunges with little ado over the Mühlibort to the Sefinen Lütschine. This is the quickest verdant way into the valley – 55 min according to the signpost. Büttlassen and Horn in the background.

▶ *"Achtung Steinschlag – Beware of falling stones." The wet and slippery gulley is best crossed in a rapid zig-zag and left speedily behind. The passage and the path up to the alps from Busen and Sefinen were already the subject of strife and litigation in the 13th century.*

box-making, weaving, spinning, pillow work and wood-carving. The vicar, Johann Unger, had roared from the pulpit in an effort to awaken in his parishioners a sense of craftmanship. It was all to no avail. The solution to the problem lay in Wyttenbach's guide, for its description of the valleys charms was attracting visitors who required, above all things, porters and sumpters on the rough, bumpy paths – strong men and local guides. And because God's wide open spaces were the valley people's favourite workshop, this kind of enterprise suited them a great deal better. From the spontaneously created trade of porter and sumpter developed the profession of the respected mountain guide. Between 1856 and 1912 Lauterbrunnen produced 126 licensed and talented guides. The vicarage had long since ceased to be able to accommodate those visiting the mountains, so hotels were built. The flourishing hotel industry obtained its cheese and butter from the farmers and employed local women to do the laundry. One thing led to another and quite suddenly the alpine co-operatives took on a new lease of life. And how the good clean alps radiated their satisfaction!

▶▶ *A walking map with suggestions for tours along mountain and lowland footpaths in the region of the Schilthorn Cableway. Further details on pp. 118–124. Information about ski runs and skiing tours on pp. 90–92.*

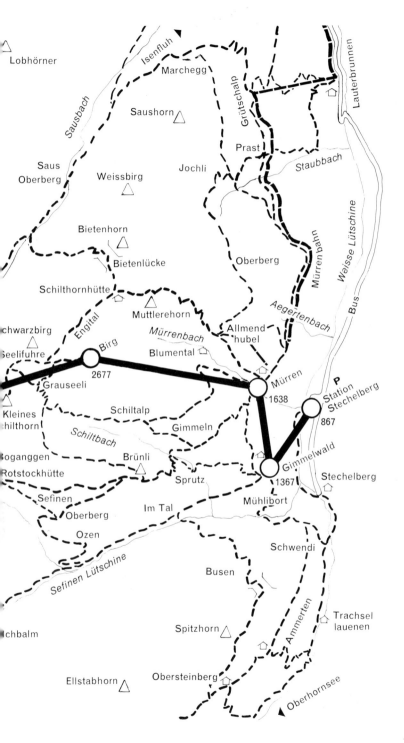

Lobhörner

Isenfluh

Marchegg

Grütschalp

Lauterbrunnen

Sausbach

Saushorn

Prast

Staubbach

Saus
Oberberg

Weissbirg

Jochli

Bietenhorn

Oberberg

Weisse Lütschine

Bietenlücke

Mürrenbahn

Schilthornhütte

Aegertenbach

Engital

Muttlerehorn

Allmend
hubel

chwarzbirg

Mürrenbach

Bus

Seelifuhre

Birg

Blumental

2677

Mürren

Grauseeli

Schiltalp

1638

P
Station
Stechelberg

Kleines
chilthorn

Gimmeln

867

Schiltbach

Gimmelwald

3oganggen

Brünli

Stechelberg

Rotstockhütte

Sprutz

1367

Sefinen

Oberberg

Im Tal

Mühlibort

Ozen

Schwendi

Sefinen Lütschine

Busen

Ammerten

chbalm

Trachsel
lauenen

Spitzhorn

Ellstabhorn

Obersteinberg

Oberhornsee

Up Hill and down Dale

The cabins of the Schilthorn cableway pass over historical countryside. For all the impressive wildness of its primitive nature, human industry has nevertheless left its stamp upon it. Each well-trodden path pursues an economic objective such as the huts on an alp or a remote pasture to be reached in a manner calculated to husband physical strength and exclude risk. For hundreds of years the valley folk have carried their loads and driven their cattle along these paths. But between them, seemingly lost and leading nowhere, narrower paths criss-cross the slopes from alp to alp for the purpose of more rapid communications. Footpaths therefore radiate from each station on the Schilthorn cableway to form a network of great variety. Few desires of the wanderer in search of the beauties of Nature and solitary quietude are left unfulfilled. But he would be well advised to take to the hills wearing well-soled boots and carrying modest provisions, a woollen jacket and some protection against rain. Among the 1:25000 maps drawn by the Swiss Topographical Department, the Schilthorn region as shown in the diagram on pp. 116/117 is to be found on Sheet 1248, "Mürren", and

◄◄ *View from the Rottal into the upper valley of the Tschingel Lütschine and the Schmadribach Falls – to today's nature reserve and the paradise of old Lauterbrunnen folktales.*
Legends tell of a once flourishing settlement in Ammerten on the left mountain slope. A first batch of Walsers came via the Wetterlücke (extreme left), Petersgrat (white section centre) or the Sefinenfurgge (at extreme right edge) from the Lötschental in 1346.

◄ *The "Lötscherglocke", dated 1483, in front of the church in Lauterbrunnen. The bell was presumed to have been borne on a yoke over the Wetterlücke.*

Sheet 1228, "Lauterbrunnen." To introduce a little order into this fine-meshed network of footpaths, the best thing would perhaps be to illuminate the valleys touched upon like the rooms in a house open upon all sides.

Let's start with the mezzanine floor, in Gimmelwald which has always lain on the path to Mürren, which always had the same number of inhabitants as Mürren and which, after the construction of the Mürren Railway, became completely isolated. Gimmelwald, with its gay flower-gardens and stone-weighed shingle rooves, is still a village straight out of a picture book. Gimmelwald also has two hotels – although the one where Friedrich W. Nietzsche slept in 1871 has disappeared. At the parting of the ways for Sefinen, the Schiltalp and Mürren, there once stood a fountain in front of the wine-garden. The fashionable guests were carried up from Stechelberg in velvet-upholstered sedans. The village's *pièce de résistance* is the warm, flower-strewn valley of the Sefinen Lütschine, encircled by the Gspaltenhorn

►► *The energetic little peak of the Schilthorn presides over the villages of Mürren, Gimmelwald and Stechelberg on the valley floor. The line of the Schilthorn Cableway follows the historic path – round the back via the south-eastern slopes. Below the Schilthorn is the "Schilt", that shield-shaped alpine hollow from which the mountain took its name. At the centre is the Blumental; above Mürren, the ski run from the Engital, like an open wound; to the right, the Winteregg and Pletschen Alps.*

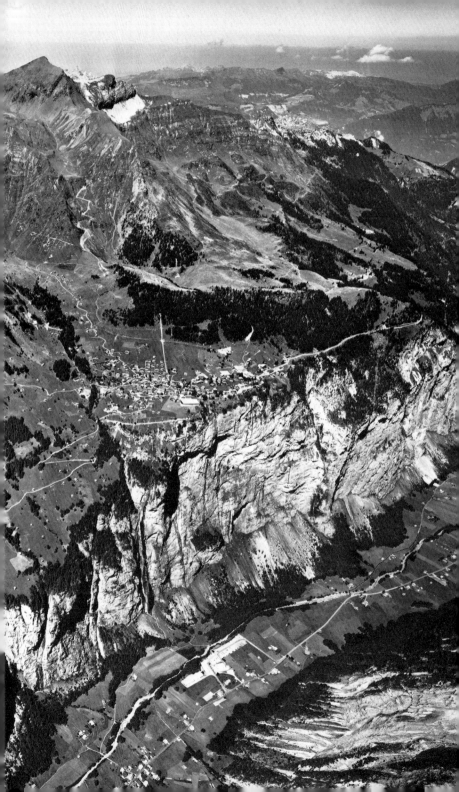

and Büttlassen, with the remote kettle of Kilchbalm and the alpine meadows above – once famous for the delicious cheese produced there –, across which the age-old Sefinenfurgge Pass leads into the Kander Valley. At the stream, the path branches off to the Busen Alp and into the valley of the Tschingel Lütschine. Thus, we have already peeped into the second room of our house, that wildly romantic mountain circus of infinite beauty which today includes a nature reserve (see pictures on pp. 81 and 118). The valley beneath the Breithorn, rich in history and woven about with legend, was settled and wooded to a great height in the Middle Ages.

Walking times from Gimmelwald Station: Kilchbalm 1½ h, Boganggen 2 h 40 min, Sefinenfurgge 5 h 10 min, Busen Alp 2½ h, Obersteinberg 3½ h, Schilt Alp 2 h, Schilthorn 5½ h, Mürren 1 h 20 min, Stechelberg 55 min.

In the heights around Mürren, the forest belt gives way to rich alpine pastureland. There are paths here that reach out spaciously towards the neighbouring treasures and are not even all that strenuous. One of the favourites is the panorama path up to Grütschalp and on to the little village of Isenfluh or to the somewhat bizarre little Sausläger Lake. One of the most beautiful of Mürren's alps, which lies dreaming on a sunny, open slope, is undoubtedly that in the Schilt above Gimmeln – ideal both for the walk and as a quiet resting place. The more ambitious will take the path up the steep slope between the Schilthorn and the crumpled crest of the Birg (p. 33) to reach the rock-fortified basin of the Grauseeli. If the ascent of the Schilthorn via Schiltalp is popular because of the charm of its delightful green meadows, the other route via the Blumental, Allmendhubel and the Engital offers the advantages of a regular ascent and the hypnotic magic of the Jungfrau. This path has the added attraction of the Schilthorn Hut, halfway between Mürren and the Schilthorn, which welcomes the wanderer to a bowl of soup or a cup of coffee.

Walking times from Mürren Station: Grütschalp Station 1 h 25 min, Saustal 2½ h, Isenfluh 2½ h, Lauterbrunnen 1½ h, Sefinenfurgge 4 h, Schilt Alp 1 h 10 min, Birg Station 3 h 20 min, Schilthorn 4 h 40 min, Schilthorn Hut 2 h 50 min, Gimmelwald 45 min.

It is hard to leave the belvedere and the open-air restaurant on the Birg with its radiantly beautiful triumvirate of Eiger, Mönch and Jungfrau, and yet it is precisely this station that is most popular as a starting point. In the grey hollow of the Seelifuhre, a decision must be taken. The easiest descent leads past the Schilthorn Hut. The alternative route leads down the steep steps below the little lake and through the Schilttal. Experienced mountaineers will head for the Bietenlücke and the passage into the Saustal (see picture on pp. 56/57). Or what about climbing the Schilthorn under your own steam? The path drives a hook into the flank of the glacier-girded slope (see picture on p. 64).

Walking times from Birg Station: Schilthorn 1 h 40 min, Mürren 2 h 40 min, Schilthorn Hut 1 h, Bietenhorn 2 h 20 min, Schilt Alp 1½ h, Gimmelwald 2 h 50 min, Seelifuhre 20 min.

◀ *Mürren. The cabin is already waiting at the station of the Schilthorn Cableway to carry the hurrying, restlessly seeking folk back to the valley and towards a fresh destination. "Come again soon," beckons the cow parsley... hum the bees – and the cone-hung spruces nod in agreement.*

▶ *The four wheels required for the onward journey are in the carpark where there is room for 1500 cars. The motorway is 16 km distant.*

The world is so beautiful and life is so short! The minute one leaves, the mountains beckon one back. And with each visit they reveal a little more of that secret of eternal growth and evolution. This is all very heady stuff and to sip it is dangerous enough – a good long draught and one is hooked for life! The Jungfrau near Mürren.

Then up to the top floor – to the Schilthorn itself which offers five more possibilities. Two routes storm the Birg and return to the Seelifuhre where they fork off to the Schiltalp or the Engital. The other three offer a view of Montblanc, skipping over stairways and steps, some of them quite deep (keep children on a rope!) along the crest to Roter Herd and a parting of the ways (see pictures on pp. 84 and 91): the lefthand path leads into the beautiful Sefinental, to the hospitable Rotstock Hut and up to the Sefinenfurgge Pass; straight ahead, it enters a completely different valley region – the romantic Spiggengrund. To the right, the blossom-filled mountain valley of Saus opens up – basking in the warmth of Aphrodite's smile and much loved by devoted Schilthorn fans. Take your pick from the treasures in that incomparable kingdom which beckons beyond the windows of the "Piz Gloria"!

Walking times from Schilthorn Station: Roter Herd 30 min, Hohkien 2 h, Kiental Post-office 4½ h (go carefully!), Boganggen and Rotstock Hut 1 h 40 min, Sefinenfurgge 3½ h, Mürren 3½ h, Saustal-Grütschalp Station 3½ h, Birg Station 1 h 10 min, Seelifuhre 45 min.

Chronological Table

1240 First mention of the "in claro fonte" valley. The clear springs near Steg in the Ey appear to have been the focal point of the old Lauterbrunnen Valley – at the meeting of the paths from Wengen, Mürren and the upper and lower valley.

1257 The names of "Lauterbrunnen" and "mons Murren" first mentioned.

1346 "Schilt" appears as the name of the alp in the hollow below the Schilthorn.

1346 Evidence of Lötschental folk in the settlements of Mürren, Gimmelwald, Trachsellauenen, Sichellauenen and Ammerten in upper Lauterbrunnental.

1349 Secret alliance between the people of Gimmelwald, Ammerten and Lauterbrunnen with Obwalden; uprising against the monastery at Interlaken. The provost seeks the support of the City of Berne.

1470–1715 Iron-mining operations on the slope to the right of Trachsellauenen.

1488 Establishment of the parish of Lauterbrunnen. The church was to be dedicated to "Sanctus Andreas ad limpidas fontes".

1528 Storming of the monastery at Interlaken. The canons fetch help in Berne and reach a property settlement. A landvogt is appointed for the Oberland.

ca. 1645 The cultivation of bread-cereals ceases in Gimmelwald and Mürren.

1653 Hearth census in Lauterbrunnental – there are 105, most of them impoverished.

1669 The Great Plague. Of an estimated 580 inhabitants in Lauterbrunnental, 360 die. Six serious epidemics have swept the valley since 1516.

1705–1805 Lead glance and zinc ore prospecting on both the valley slopes near Trachsellauenen.

1732 The era of Alpine appreciation dawns with Haller's poem, "Die Alpen".

1776 Only a few dwellings remain of once-significant Ammerten.

1783 Mürren has 26 households and 92 inhabitants, and was thought to be the best-endowed village in the valley; 110 cows wintered. Gimmelwald has 18 households and 75 inhabitants; 118 cows wintered. Wine, entertainment, coffee and tobacco not known. No poor. Mürren and Gimmelwald share a school.

1811 Mountaineering starts in Lauterbrunnen. First ascent of the Jungfrau (3. 8.).

ca. 1823 Hotel trade begins in the Lauterbrunnen Valley – first tavern, the "Steinbock".

1835 First steamship on the Lake of Thoune. Shortens journey to Bernese Oberland.

1839 Sumpter path to Lauterbrunnen is gradually made carriageable.

1856 20 licensed mountain guides registered in Lauterbrunnen.

1857 Winteregg alpine co-operative builds the "Silberhorn", the first hotel in Mürren.

1864 Post starts being delivered daily in Mürren in summer because of the tourists.

1869 Opening of Gimmelwald's first hotel, the "Schilthorn", with 50 beds.

1883 Xaver Imfeld, engineer, draws the panorama seen from the Schilthorn.

1887 Leonhard Heer of Bienne, who later built the Gornergrat and Wengernalp Railways, applies with F. Marti, Frey & Haag for a licence to build the Mürren Railway. (28. 2.).

1887 Zschokke & Co., Aarau, announce their application for a licence, accompanied by financial statement, for construction of a direct railway from Interlaken to Mürren.

1887 Lauterbrunnen decides by 178 votes to petition for rejection of the Mürren railway project as it would jeopardize the incomes of the guides, coachmen, porters, horse-leaders and inn-keepers in the upper village (27. 3.). A counter petition is filed by 219 citizens who argued that initial income losses would be made good later (18. 4.).

1890 Opening of the Bernese Oberland Railway authorized in 1887. Steam-operated.

1891 Concession granted the Bodencreditanstalt, Berne, for a narrow-gauge railway from Lauterbrunnen to Visp, with summit tunnel at 2213 m. Prolonged till 1897.

1891 Opening of Mürren Railway (14. 8.) authorized on 18th June 1887.

1893 Opening of the Thoune–Spiez–Interlaken railway line. Opening of the Wengernalp and Schynige Platte Railways.

1894 Adolf Guyer-Zeller, Zurich, obtains the licence to build the Jungfrau Railway.

1896 Breithorn Railway concession transferred to F. Michel, Interlaken; summit tunnel at 1590 m. (14. 12.). Concession maintained till 1906.

1898 First free balloon flight over the Alps from Sion to Langres by Edouard Spelterini.

1903 First winter season – without railway – in Mürren. Sledging, skating, skiing.

1904 Spelterini's balloon flight from Eigergletscher Station into the Rhône Valley and to Adelboden.

1906 Mürren hoteliers apply for a licence to build an aerial cableway from Stegmatten near Lauterbrunnen to Mürren (7. 8.). 800 m difference in altitude.

1908 Opening of first passenger ropeway in Switzerland, on the Wetterhorn.

1908 Otto Meyer, surveyor and topographer, asks the Federal Council on behalf of Gimmelwald and the planned co-operative, if a Stechelberg–Gimmelwald–Mürren aerial cableway needs a concession if initially used only for freight.

1908 Federal Council to issue no further aerial cableway concessions until operational experience on the Wetterhorn is available (3. 4.). Berne cantonal government opposes Stegmatten–Mürren cableway (1. 4.).
Federal railways department advises Gimmelwald against an application.

1910 Spelterini's balloon flight from Mürren to the Turin region.

1910 Mürren Railway starts regular winter operations – previously only May–October.

1912 Opening of the Mürren–Allmendhubel Funicular. Bob-run.

1913 44 licensed mountain guides in Lauterbrunnen.

1926 Two Mürren hotels burnt to the ground in November.

1928 First Inferno Race from Schilthorn to Lauterbrunnen. 2000 m difference in altitude.

1930 Mürren has 243 inhabitants, Gimmelwald 228.

1931 First World Skiing Championships (FIS) and Arlberg-Kandahar Race in Mürren.

1937 Construction of the Schiltgrat ski-lift; Kandahar racing run.

1948 Planned Stechelberg–Gimmelwald road rejected as too expensive.

1956 Project for a Gimmelwald–Mürren chairlift; question of a ski-lift studied.

1957 Another balloon flight over the Alps – Fred Dolder takes off in Mürren.
Physical training centre opened by the Schweizerische Landesverband für Leibesübungen (SLL).

1959 2nd project for a Stechelberg–Gimmelwald aerial cableway (to-and-fro system) with 10-passenger cabins, co-operative-run. No subsidies available for building.

1959 Concession requested for Allmendhubel–Engital cableway, to be extended later.

1959 Application for Stechelberg–Gimmelwald–Mürren–Birg–Schilthorn cableway. Takeover of the interests in the co-operative project (3. 10.).

1961 Concession granted for the four-section Schilthorn cableway (23. 10.).

1962 Foundation of Schilthornbahn AG with Fr. 8 million share capital, divided into 16,000 bearer shares at sFr. 500.– (28. 4.).
Building contract with Von Roll who agree to build the cableway at an all-in rate of sFr. 5.05 million, excluding far-reaching changes (28. 4.).

1962 1st International High Alpine Ballooning Weeks in Mürren.

1965 Opening of the first three sections of the Schilthorn cableway.

1967 Completion of the Schilthorn cableway right up to the peak (12. 6.).

Tables

Maps and Panoramas

Acknowledgements

This book has been written and produced with the help of the Schilthorn Cableway. Management, technical staff and the secretary were unfailingly willing to give friendly and patient explanations and to supply documentation whenever a question arose concerning the functioning or the history of the cableway. The author is most grateful to all of them. A special word of thanks goes to the Managing Director, Mr. Paul Eggenberg, and the Chairman of the Board, Mr. Ernst Feuz, who took a lively interest in the progress of the book and, by most generously giving the author *carte blanche,* intensified the pleasure of coaxing the Schilthorn cableway between the covers of a book.

Many of the pictures come from the archives of the Schilthornbahn AG in Mürren (among the photographers are Willi Burkhardt Buochs, Rolf Krebs Kirchdorf, W.M. Kaenel Mürren, Von Roll Berne). A considerable number of illustrations, above all the coloured ones and the frontispiece, were specially made for this book by the author herself. Other documents and photographs come from the Swiss National Tourist Office Zurich, Verkehrsverein Mürren, Kurt Huggler Mürren, J. Zwahlen Mürren, Hermann Mölders Mürren, Foto Bavaria, Hans Steiner Berne, Gyger Adelboden, Schweiz. Seilindustrie AG Schaffhausen, Werner Friedli Brüttisellen, Edmund Wunderlich Berne, Hanni Steiner Lauterbrunnen, Hilda Wyss Mürren, the Jungfrau Railway (H. Meier Thoune), Federal Copyright Department Berne, Federal Archives Berne and Swissair Photo AG Zurich.